Chip's Sensors Detected a Hand on His Shoulder....

The hand jerked Chip around. He could have refused to turn, but he would have risked revealing that his android body weighed 420 pounds!

Chip came face to face with an angry man wearing a sweatshirt labeled "Harbor Junior High COACH."

"What's your name, kid?" growled the big man.

"My name is Chip," answered the android. "This is my first day at school."

The man ran his hand through his thick black hair. He tried unsuccessfully to calm down. "It's going to be your last day," he said, "or my name isn't Mr. Duckworth."

"And if it isn't my last day," asked Chip, attempting to sort out the logic, "then what is your name?"

"Your name is going to be mud if you don't tell me why you smashed my trophy case!" roared Mr. Duckworth.

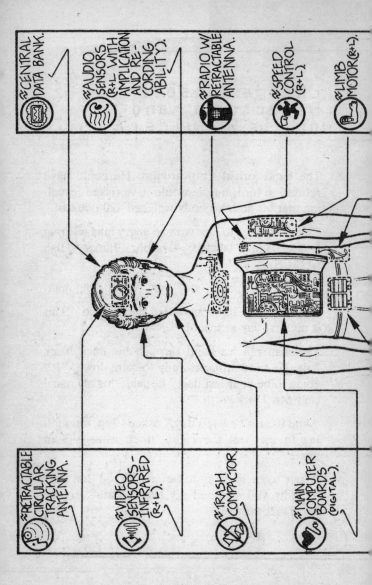

CENTRAL DATA BANK.

AUDIO SENSORS (R+L) WITH AMPLICATION AND RE-CORDING ABILITY).

RADIO W/ RETRACTABLE ANTENNA.

SPEED CONTROL (R+L)

LIMB MOTOR (R+L).

RETRACTABLE CIRCULAR TRACKING ANTENNA.

VIDEO SENSORS-INFRARED (R+L).

TRASH COMPACTOR.

MAIN COMPUTER BOARDS (DIGITAL).

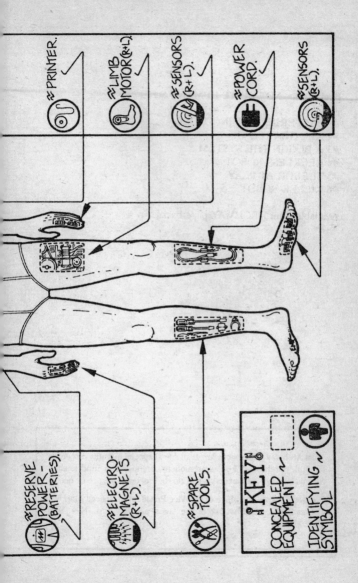

PRINTER.

LIMB MOTOR (R+L).

SENSORS (R+L).

POWER CORD.

SENSORS (R+L).

RESERVE POWER-(BATTERIES).

ELECTRO-MAGNETS (R+L).

SPARE TOOLS.

KEY

CONCEALED EQUIPMENT

IDENTIFYING SYMBOL

Books in the NOT QUITE HUMAN™ Series

Available from ARCHWAY paperbacks

NOT QUITE HUMAN™
#1
BATTERIES NOT INCLUDED

Produced by
THE PHILIP LIEF GROUP,
INC.

SETH McEVOY

AN ARCHWAY PAPERBACK
Published by POCKET BOOKS • NEW YORK

AN ARCHWAY PAPERBACK *Original*

An Archway Paperback published by
POCKET BOOKS, a division of Simon & Schuster, Inc.
1230 Avenue of the Americas, New York, N.Y. 10020

Copyright © 1985 by The Philip Lief Group, Inc.,
319 East 52nd Street, New York, N.Y. 10022
Cover artwork copyright © 1985 Gary Ruddell
Frontispiece copyright © 1985 Ted Enik
Produced by The Philip Lief Group, Inc.
Based on characters created by Kevin Osborn

ISBN: 0-671-65760-7

First Archway Paperback printing November 1985

10 9 8 7 6 5 4

AN ARCHWAY PAPERBACK and colophon are
registered trademarks of Simon & Schuster, Inc.

NOT QUITE HUMAN® is a trademark
of Simon & Schuster, Inc.

Printed in the U.S.A.

IL 5+

Dedication

This book is dedicated to Laure Smith,
whose insight, help, and encouragement
made all the difference.

Special thanks to: Andrea Brown,
Philip Lief, Kevin Osborn,
Pat MacDonald, and Ron Buehl.

BATTERIES
NOT INCLUDED

Diary—September 7

My greatest achievement is finally finished.

I've created the C-13 integrated electrologic android and it looks exactly like a 13-year-old boy. He's programmed to imitate every action of a typical teenager. He can walk, talk, look, listen, and think.

Of course, his thinking is only as good as I have made it, but my android creation should be able to act like a normal human being. No one will know that he's not quite human, except my daughter Becky and myself.

The android's metal surface is covered with a high-resolution, multiflex plastic skin that is warm to the touch, and his blond hair and blue eyes look so real that no one will suspect they are made of nylon. He can stay in contact with me by his internal interface radio. His C-13 microbatteries will keep him operating for up to ten hours before they'll need recharging, and he has many other unusual abilities which are still in the experimental stage. I hope that my creation will show the world that androids can perform many tasks as well as human beings can, and can offer a valuable service to society.

To complete this experiment, I've moved to a new town and have enrolled the android as an eighth grader at Harbor Junior High. As the new science teacher there, I can guard his secret and keep a close watch on him. Becky is starting seventh grade at the same school and I know she'll look out for my creation. She's mature and responsible and has been a big help to me since her mother passed away.

I've named the android Chip. Tomorrow is his first day at school; I sincerely hope that he performs well.

Dr. Jonas Carson

CHAPTER 1

Chip scanned the school corridor. He could see forty-seven humans ahead of him. His pattern-recognition program told him that forty-five of them were students and that the two taller ones were teachers.

As his synchronized sector motors moved him down the red brick corridor, a freckle-faced boy stepped in front of him and asked, "Do you know where Room three-twenty-six is?"

Chip's special electrologic memory banks included a complete map of Harbor Junior High. Clutching his books against his yellow sweater, the android answered, "Walk fifty-two feet straight ahead, turn right, climb eighty-eight steps, turn left, walk seventeen feet and turn right."

3

"You're putting me on!" said the boy.

Chip's conversation computer program analyzed the remark. According to his verbal data files, "putting on" was something you did with clothes. Did the boy want to be put on like a jacket? "Do you want me to carry you to Room three-twenty-six?" inquired Chip, holding out his arms. He had the ability to lift 500 pounds and his sensors told him that the boy weighed much less.

Laughing out loud, the boy answered, "No! I think I can walk on my own two feet. I just wanted to know where my class was."

"My name is Chip," said the android. His conversation program told him to say this when no one asked him a specific question.

"Hi, Chip," said the boy. "My name's Pete. I'd better hurry or I'll never find my class." Pete turned around and rushed toward the stairway muttering, "Climb eighty-eight steps! That guy must be some kind of weirdo!"

Chip checked the time on his internal clock. It was 7:50. His first class was at 8:00. Chip picked up speed as he headed down the hall. All of a sudden, one of the sector motors in his left leg abruptly slowed down. Chip stumbled forward and slammed into a gray metal locker. *Wham!*

Something was wrong! Chip conducted a quick emergency scan of all his circuits and

4

calculated that his voltage levels were dangerously low. At the rate they were falling, he only had a few minutes before his microbatteries would go dead! Without power, Chip's memory circuits would fail and his entire operating system would crash.

His dynakinetic circuits immediately told him this was an extremely dangerous situation, so he activated his internal radio and called his father in his science class. *Battery level 1.32 falling at .09 per minute,* he broadcasted.

Dr. Carson had his receiving radio safely hidden in the drawer of his desk and it was tuned to Chip's frequency. Luckily his first class hadn't started, so Dr. Carson could easily answer the call. He pulled the keys from the pocket of his brown sports coat and fumbled with the lock on the drawer. His glasses slid down his nose as he whispered nervously into the radio's microphone. "There must have been a malfunction in the charging circuit," he said to Chip. "Find a wall socket and insert your auxiliary power recharging plug into it, but make sure no one is watching. Hurry!"

Acknowledge, replied Chip. He began searching desperately for a wall socket. He could see plenty of outlets, but there were always people nearby.

When the bell rang, the students darted into their rooms. Using most of his remaining power, Chip turned on his telescopic vision. He spotted a wall socket in a dark corner at the end of the hall and headed straight for it.

No one was in sight. Chip pulled up his blue corduroy pants and popped open a small hatch in his leg. His last ounces of power were draining away as he slowly unreeled a cord and plugged it into the socket. The electricity surged into his charging unit and his energy was instantly restored. A quick estimate of his operating system showed he could function at full power for the rest of the school day.

Chip reeled the cord back into his leg and hurried to his first class. He was already late. His father had programmed him to be on time whenever possible, but he had given Chip a data file of good excuses just in case.

Crash! Chip heard a strange noise coming from the gym, but it was too far away for him to recognize. With his audio record-and-replay circuit, he listened to the noise over again. Played back louder, he discovered it matched the sound pattern of breaking glass!

According to the data file in Chip's computer brain, his specific order for this sound read: "Glass that is breaking can injure humans. You must help any human who is injured."

Chip raced toward the gym. The corridors were empty, so he could move as fast as his motor-driven legs would carry him—70 miles per hour! Zooming around a corner, he skidded across a floorful of broken glass. Fortunately the android's internal gyroscope prevented him from crashing to the floor. He stopped to investigate.

No one was in the corridor. Chip analyzed the situation and determined that the glass had come from a display case in the wall. The case was empty. Since there was no danger to humans, Chip's main program told him to return to his earlier priority—to get to class.

But before Chip could turn around, the sensors in his shoulder detected a hand. He could tell it was the hand of an adult human, and that the hand was gripping him very tightly.

The hand jerked Chip's shoulder around. He could have refused to turn, but he would have risked revealing that his android body weighed 420 pounds!

Chip came face to face with a muscular adult wearing a red sweat shirt labeled "Harbor Junior High COACH." From the man's expression, Chip could tell that this human was angry.

"What's your name, kid?" growled the big man.

"My name is Chip," answered the android. "This is my first day at school."

The man ran his hand through his thick black hair. "It's going to be your last day," he yelled, "or my name isn't Mr. Duckworth."

"And if it *isn't* my last day," asked Chip, attempting to sort out the logic, "then what *is* your name?"

"Your name is going to be mud if you don't tell me why you smashed my trophy case!"

"My name will always be Chip," answered the mechanical boy. "It can't change. Although sometimes women change their names when they get married."

"Come on, why did you do it?" asked Mr. Duckworth.

"I can't answer that," replied Chip.

"You'll answer me or I'll skin you alive!"

"You'll skin me a live what?" said Chip, innocently. "Which animal are you going to skin if I don't answer you?"

"I'm going to skin *you*," snapped Mr. Duckworth. "All my trophies are gone! Where are they?"

The word "trophy" was not in Chip's data banks, but he was programmed to try to be helpful. He scanned the corridors. "Is that one down there?" he asked.

"No, that's a drinking fountain!" yelled the teacher. "Are you crazy or what?"

"I must be what," answered Chip, because his programming told him he wasn't crazy.

"What?" roared Mr. Duckworth.

"What," repeated Chip.

Mr. Duckworth yanked Chip's yellow sweater. "Who took my trophies?"

8

"I don't know," answered the android.

"Okay, kid," grumbled the teacher, "then did you see who stole them?"

At that moment, Chip's circuits, weakened by his earlier power loss, malfunctioned, but he calculated that a spare circuit could be substituted and the damage repaired.

"Answer me," shouted Mr. Duckworth.

Still unable to speak, Chip remained silent. His internal operating system was exchanging the circuits.

In a fit of anger, Mr. Duckworth yelled, "If you don't answer me I'll forget what the school rules are and—"

Pop! The repair was made and the mechanical boy was able to speak again. "My name is Chip," he said, answering an earlier question. During the circuit changeover a tiny part of his memory had been erased and now he couldn't remember why he was standing there.

"Okay, kid, if that's the way you want to play it—Chip what?"

"What?"

"Don't start that again! What's your last name?"

"Carson," answered Chip. "What's yours?"

"Mr. Duckworth, and you won't forget it."

"I won't forget it," repeated Chip flatly. Just to be sure, he made an extra copy of Mr. Duckworth's name and face in a spare memory bank.

9

The teacher was silent for a moment. He looked at Chip suspiciously. Finally he said, "Usually I'd send a kid like you to the principal's office, but I think I'll take *you* to Dr. Stromberg. He's the school psychologist. Maybe he can get the truth out of you."

Before Chip could protest, Mr. Duckworth took him by the shoulder and marched him down the hallway. The android was programmed to obey all adults, so he went quietly, especially after the gym teacher told him to shut up.

Mr. Duckworth opened the green metal door to Dr. Stromberg's office, and shoved Chip inside. "This one's yours, Stromberg," he said. "I want you to get the truth out of this little creep."

Dr. Stromberg glanced over tops of his thick round glasses and sighed. "What's the problem, Duckworth? Somebody steal one of your whistles again?"

"No, they didn't steal one of my whistles again. They stole thousands of dollars worth of silver sports trophies, okay? This boy was the only witness and he won't say a word. He's probably in on it."

Dr. Stromberg smiled. "Leave him to me, Duckworth. This boy doesn't look so bad."

"You always say that. If you don't get a

10

confession out of him in an hour, the police will." He stomped out of the office and slammed the door behind him.

Turning to Chip, Dr. Stromberg asked in a kindly voice, "Now, what's your name?"

"My name is Chip," answered the android.

CHAPTER 2

Dr. Stromberg opened his black notebook, smiled and said, "Now tell me what happened."

"When?" asked Chip.

"Tell me everything that happened this morning," replied the psychologist.

Chip cross-referenced his memory banks with his system clock. *Nothing!* "I don't know," answered Chip sincerely.

"Think back to the first thing you remember," encouraged Dr. Stromberg.

Chip switched his audio recording system to replay. Even though his memory had been erased, his audio system was on an auxiliary circuit board. "My name is Chip," he said in his own voice. Then he switched to Mr. Duckworth's voice and said, "Okay, kid, if that's the way you want to play it—Chip what?" He repeated the rest of the conversation, ending with Dr. Stromberg's, "Think back to the first thing you remember."

Dr. Stromberg sighed. "I see you have a talent for dramatics," he said. "But what happened before that?"

"I don't know," said Chip sincerely.

"What *do* you know?"

"The Declaration of Independence was adopted on July 4, 1776," he began. "George Washington was the first president of the United States and was inaugurated on April 30, 1789. He was reelected in 1793—"

"This isn't social studies class, Chip!" interrupted Dr. Stromberg.

"It's eight-forty," chimed Chip. "That's when social studies class is scheduled."

"The only thing I'm interested in is Mr. Duckworth's trophies. What can you tell me about them?"

"Mr. Duckworth said they were worth thousands of dollars. And they were stolen," Chip replied. "But I don't know what trophies are."

Patiently, the psychologist explained, "They are silver cups that our athletic teams have won in competitions."

"Where are they?" asked Chip.

"I'm supposed to ask you that question!" yelled Dr. Stromberg.

Chip said nothing.

After waiting patiently, Dr. Stromberg finally continued, "Now, tell me where the trophies are."

"I've never seen them," answered Chip.

At that moment, Mr. Duckworth poked his head through the green door. "Have you cracked him yet?" he asked.

"He doesn't seem to know anything . . . except his history lesson!" said the psychologist. "Are you sure he's involved? He doesn't show any of the usual signs of guilt."

"Then why wasn't he in class?" answered Mr. Duckworth triumphantly.

"That's a good question," said Dr. Stromberg. Turning to Chip, he asked, "Why weren't you in class?"

Chip examined his electrologic memory banks. He could not remember anything about today at all. However, his father had given him an excuse file which was in a different part of his memory banks. The android replied, "I couldn't find my class. Today is my first day here at Harbor Junior High."

Dr. Stromberg closed his notebook and said, "There, Mr. Duckworth! He's a new student and he was lost. I seriously doubt that a new student would steal your precious trophies."

"Nonsense!" shouted the gym teacher. "I'll show you how to find out things. Stand up," he ordered Chip.

Chip rose. Mr. Duckworth grabbed him by the shoulders and shook him back and forth.

"Jim!" yelled Dr. Stromberg. "You can't do that here!"

Mr. Duckworth ignored the psychologist. "Tell me what happened!" he demanded. He squeezed the android's shoulders together. Hidden inside Chip's armpit was a secret speed switch, set on normal.

Click! Mr. Duckworth accidentally tripped the switch. Suddenly all of Chip's integrated electrologic systems were running three times faster than normal!

Chip's father had carefully programmed him to do a series of emergency testing exercises whenever the speed switch was changed. This was to make sure that all his body systems were operating properly.

Suddenly Chip threw out his left arm—at a speed three times faster than a human. *Pow!* He smashed into Mr. Duckworth and hurled him into a chair.

Mr. Duckworth jumped up and tried to grab Chip, but the boy android was wildly going through his exercises. He threw his right arm up automatically—and crashed into the gym teacher's chin.

Sock! He knocked Mr. Duckworth across the office! The gym teacher shook his head as he staggered to his feet. He watched from a safe

15

distance as Chip finished testing his arms and legs.

When Chip finally came to a halt, Mr. Duckworth announced, "I'm getting the police!"

"Maybe you'd better wait," said Dr. Stromberg. "You had no right to shake him like that! You know our school has a strict policy against teachers striking students."

"That kid must know some fancy kind of judo," muttered Mr. Duckworth. He straightened his sweat shirt.

Dr. Stromberg looked at Chip with concern. "Are you all right, son? Mr. Duckworth didn't hurt you, did he?"

"What about me?" interrupted the gym teacher.

"You're a former football player," said Dr. Stromberg with a smile. "Nothing can hurt you. I've heard you say so many times." He turned back to Chip. "Are you all right?"

Chip could not understand what the psychologist was saying. All of his systems were still operating at three times normal speed, and Dr. Stromberg's voice sounded like a long, drawn-out buzz.

"MYNAMEISCHIP," he said very quickly. But to the humans in the room it sounded like a high-pitched squeak.

"You've upset him!" said Dr. Stromberg an-

16

grily. Then, in a soothing tone, he said to the mechanical boy, "No one will hurt you, Chip. Sit down and relax. I'm sure Mr. Duckworth didn't mean to frighten you."

Chip still didn't understand anything that was going on around him. All his android electro-logic brain could perceive was that he was being talked to in long, drawn-out buzzes. The bald man behind the desk seemed to be friendly and the muscular man standing in front of him seemed unfriendly. His internal clock told him it was 8:55 and time to go to his next class.

But Mr. Duckworth was blocking the door, so Chip couldn't leave. His father had given him strict instructions not to push humans out of the way. Chip could not figure out what to do. His last resort was to contact his father. Turning on his internal interface radio, Chip silently sent the message, "EMERGENCY. IAMTRAPPED. HELPME."

Fortunately, Dr. Carson's class had just let out and he was standing next to the radio hidden in his desk. He unlocked his desk and his wavy brown hair fell forward as he tuned the dials, trying to receive the garbled message. Dr. Carson couldn't understand Chip either, but he had a voice-activated tape recorder hooked up to the radio in case Chip sent a message while he was busy.

He played the tape back at slow speed. "I

17

never should have put that secret speed switch in such a vulnerable place," he said to himself, when he finally understood the message.

"Where are you, Chip?" Dr. Carson said into the tape recorder. Then he played the recording back at high speed into the radio.

Chip examined the map of the building in his memory banks and gave the coordinates of his location to his father. Dr. Carson told the android to sit quietly and wait.

Chip sat quietly and waited.

Meanwhile, Mr. Duckworth was arguing with Dr. Stromberg. "That boy's a menace!" he shouted. "I could've been seriously injured."

"You could've injured *him,* Duckworth! You'll be lucky if his parents don't sue the school!"

"Well, he's still a prime suspect in the trophy theft. I can tell a bad kid when I see one."

At that moment the phone rang. Dr. Stromberg picked it up and talked for a few minutes. "Looks like you're wrong about that, too," he said. "The police are already investigating the case. They said the footprints in the crushed glass around the trophy case clearly show three different people at the scene of the crime. Two of those people approached the trophy case, turned around, and returned down the hallway toward my office. From what you told the police, that sounds like you and Chip. The impressions made by the feet of the *third* person, however, only lead *away* from the trophy case, and in the opposite direction of yours and Chip's."

"So? What does that prove?" Mr. Duckworth stormed.

"Don't you see?" Dr. Stromberg explained. "The third person, presumably the thief, must have arrived *before* the glass was broken and left *after* breaking into the trophy case. Chip must be innocent."

Mr. Duckworth glared angrily at Chip. "That's not proof enough for me. Listen, kid, I'm going to be watching every move you make, and I'll prove *you* were the one who stole those trophies if it's the last thing I do!" He left, slamming the door behind him.

Dr. Stromberg sat back in his chair. "Mr. Duckworth jumped to conclusions, but he didn't mean any harm," he said. "He's just upset about his trophies."

Chip said nothing. His instructions from his father were to sit quietly and wait.

"Tell me about yourself. Where did you live before you came here?"

There was no answer. Dr. Stromberg continued, "I know you're upset, but I hope you'll understand that Mr. Duckworth didn't—"

There was a knock at the door. "I'm talking to a student," Dr. Stromberg called.

"It's Jonas Carson. Is my son in there?" said the voice on the other side of the door.

"Is your son's name Chip?" asked the psychologist.

"Yes, it is." Dr. Carson walked in and rushed to Chip. "Are you all right, son?" He furtively reached under Chip's armpit and pushed the speed switch back to normal. "Are you all right?" he repeated.

"Sure, Dad. Should I go to math class now?" answered Chip. His systems were back to normal.

Dr. Carson hid his relief as he turned to the psychologist, extended his hand, and said, "I'm Jonas Carson, the new science teacher. This is my son, Chip. Has there been any trouble?"

The psychologist stood up and shook Dr. Carson's hand. "Glad to meet you. I'm Arthur Stromberg. Chip had a run-in with Mr. Duckworth, the gym teacher, over some stolen trophies, but your boy had nothing to do with it."

"Can he go now? It's his first day here and I don't want him to miss any more classes," said Dr. Carson, relieved that Chip had not given himself away. "Go to your next class now, Chip."

"Okay, Dad." Chip headed for his next class.

When the android was gone, Dr. Stromberg explained what had happened. "Please don't be upset with Mr. Duckworth's behavior. Those trophies mean everything to him."

"I understand," said Dr. Carson. "I don't want to make trouble on my first day here, but if

20

he ever lays a hand on Chip again, he'll be sorry."

"Chip seemed quite upset, but as soon as you arrived, he calmed down," said Dr. Stromberg.

"He's easily confused," said Dr. Carson. "Since his mother died two years ago, it's been hard on him. If you ever see him doing anything that seems, well, strange or odd, let me know immediately."

"Of course. You can count on me," answered Dr. Stromberg.

Looking at the clock on the wall, Dr. Carson said, "Thanks. I'd better be getting back to class. It's my first day here too!"

"I'm glad you've joined the faculty," responded Dr. Stromberg. "I think you'll like it here."

"Thanks," said Chip's father as he left the office.

After Dr. Carson left, the psychologist wrote in his black notebook, "Something's not quite normal about Chip Carson. I can't put my finger on it."

CHAPTER 3

Chip entered his math class. He scanned the room and found an empty seat, sat down, and put his motors on idle to conserve battery power.

A dark-haired girl was sitting next to him. "Hi, I'm Jenny Driscoll," she said. "What's your name?"

It took the boy android a moment to realize she was speaking to him. He activated his speech mechanism and said, "My name is Chip Carson. This is my first day at Harbor Junior High."

"A new kid, huh?" replied Jenny. "Well, Harbor can't be any worse than the place you came from. But I bet you didn't have robberies there. Did you hear about the stolen trophies?"

"Yes," answered Chip.

"Someone's going to get in big trouble for that!" she added, as she opened a green notebook and took out a pencil. "I just hate math! I've heard that this teacher, Ms. Buzzi, gives out tons of homework."

"Even one ton is too much for a single person to carry," said Chip. "Will Ms. Buzzi deliver it in a truck?"

Jenny laughed. "It'll just seem like a ton," she said. "Look out, here she comes now!"

Ms. Buzzi marched through the door, her blue suit moving stiffly.

She began to call roll, and the class quieted down. Books were passed out and Ms. Buzzi immediately began her lecture. She explained the entire algebra lesson without changing her stern expression. Near the end of class, just as Jenny Driscoll had predicted, homework was assigned.

"Most teachers wait a day or two," whispered Jenny. "What a jerk!"

"Jerk?" said Chip aloud. "Is something shaking?"

Ms. Buzzi stopped lecturing. "Who was talking?" she asked.

"You were," Chip answered.

Ms. Buzzi frowned. "What's your name, young man?"

"Chip Carson," answered the android.

23

"Don't talk back to me like that, Mr. Carson."

"You asked a question," replied Chip. "Do you want me to answer your questions?"

"Please raise your hand first. Do you understand?" snapped Ms. Buzzi.

Chip raised his hand.

"What is it, Mr. Carson?"

"Yes," said Chip.

"Yes what?"

Chip raised his hand again.

"Yes, Mr. Carson?" said Ms. Buzzi.

"Yes, I understand," answered Chip.

The class laughed. "Be quiet, Chip," whispered Jenny. "She's got a bad temper."

"That's enough out of you," said Ms. Buzzi. "I know you're just trying to waste my time, so I'll give you all five more homework problems for tomorrow."

The class groaned while she wrote the extra work on the board. When the bell rang, two kids came over to Chip.

"Hey, don't bug her again," said a tall brown-haired boy.

A girl in a blue sweater and jeans snapped, "Yeah, we don't want to do any extra homework."

"He didn't mean any harm," answered Jenny. "He's new here. Give him a break."

Chip looked at Jenny and said, "I don't want to be broken."

"Then promise you won't bother Ms. Buzzi," said the tall boy.

"I won't bother her," answered Chip.

"Come on, we've got to get to our next class," said Jenny. "What's yours, Chip?"

"Art in Room two-fifteen," answered the android. Checking his clock, he said, "Class starts in three minutes and fifty-two seconds."

"See you later, then," replied Jenny.

"When?" asked Chip.

"Lunch, probably, if you don't mind sitting with a bunch of rowdy kids."

"Okay," answered the android.

The rest of Chip's first day went smoothly. Art class was a success. When paper and pencils were handed out, Chip used his random drawing program to make elaborate pictures. The teacher liked Chip's artwork so much he put it up on the bulletin board.

Chip had no need for food, but his father had programmed him to go to lunch and pretend to eat so that no one would think he was unusual. His younger sister Becky had a later lunch break, so he accepted Jenny's offer to sit with her and her friends, Cristy, P.J., Scott, Alex, Erin, and Mario. The android found an empty chair next to Jenny. As he sat down with his tray of food, a short girl with long red hair pulled out the chair next to him.

"Aren't you new here?" she asked. "Didn't I see you in my art class?"

25

"Yes," answered Chip as he had been programmed to respond. "My father, sister, and I just moved to Harbor City."

"Great!" said the girl, setting her orange lunch tray on the table. "We could use some new faces around here, especially cute ones."

"Oh, no!" said Mario, slapping his hand against his forehead. "Here she goes again. It looks like Chip is going to get the Erin treatment this time."

"Cut it out," snapped P.J., a girl with curly blond hair. "Erin's just being friendly."

"If that's what you want to call it," Mario replied with a laugh. "But I'd say she's out to snare another guy."

"Sure, Mario," said P.J., rolling her eyes. "I bet you're just jealous." She turned to Chip and added, "Don't pay any attention to him. He's just our resident grump."

"Oh, he's all right," said Jenny to Chip. Then she raised her voice so the whole table could hear her. "I'm sure you've all noticed Chip here. He's new in town, and his father is the new science teacher."

"Hey, maybe you could convince your father to give me an A," said Scott, who was sitting across from Chip.

"No way," said Alex. "If you ever got an A the entire school would go into shock for weeks."

26

"Stranger things have happened," answered Scott.

"Not in the last twelve thousand years," said Cristy from the end of the table.

Scott scowled at her as he bit into his sandwich.

Chip appeared to be eating by putting food into his mouth, chewing, and swallowing. A miniature oral trash compactor took care of the food from there. Chip consumed everything on his tray and emptied the dishes onto the conveyor belt just like the other kids did.

Then everyone said goodbye as they headed out the cafeteria door and went on to their next class.

The mechanical boy managed to get through English, study hall, and biology without any more trouble.

As he collected his books from his locker after his last class, Mr. Duckworth suddenly appeared. "Just because the police think some other kids stole my trophies, don't think that I'm fooled!" he said. "I've got my eye on you, and I'll be watching every move you make, Carson."

"Which eye?" asked Chip.

Mr. Duckworth stormed off without answering.

Dr. Carson and Becky had after-school meetings that day, so the android followed the digital

27

map in his electrologic memory banks as he walked home.

When he arrived at the Carsons' split-level, redwood house, Chip plugged himself into the battery recharger and waited for his father to arrive.

About an hour later, Dr. Carson came home. "Follow me to the lab, Chip," said the scientist. "I want to check you over and see what the problem is."

Chip walked obediently behind his creator. When they were downstairs, Dr. Carson instructed the android to sit next to an elaborate computer. He pulled off Chip's sweater, unbuttoned his shirt, and opened a large hatch in his chest.

First the scientist attached wires from Chip's dynakinetic circuits to the computer on the desk. As Dr. Carson typed away at the terminal, he transferred the data records of Chip's activities to floppy disks for later study.

Then he switched the android off and began examining the power supply. "The batteries failed this morning, but it mustn't happen again!" he said to himself. "I've been working on this project for over twelve years. This is just a little setback, and I'm not going to let it stop me now." He removed the master circuit board which contained the unique electrologic memory chips that gave Chip the ability to function.

28

"My lifelong dream has been to create the most advanced android ever. This is the ultimate test: if Chip can make it through junior high school, he can make it through anything."

Dr. Carson traced the circuits and found some loose insulation on one of the battery pack wires. "That'll teach me to use army surplus," he chuckled, as he attached new wires.

Dr. Carson removed Chip's shirt and lifted up his left arm. "And this speed switch must be better protected." He rummaged around in a giant box full of electronic junk and found a round cover for the switch. He drilled a few holes, screwed it in place, and tested the switch. "Perfect!" he exclaimed. "Now the speed switch can't be accidentally tripped again unless this cover's removed."

Dr. Carson then made several changes in the speed unit's circuitry so that if the android's motors went into high-speed operation, his voice and hearing circuits would continue to function normally. He also changed the synchronized sector motor controls so that they could operate independently if necessary.

Turning Chip's power back on again, Dr. Carson said, "How are you feeling, Chip?"

The android ran through his macro-monitoring program and examined all his circuits. "Excellent, Dad. No problems detected."

29

"Do you remember what happened in Dr. Stromberg's office?" asked his father.

Chip recited the morning's events that were contained in his electrologic memory banks.

"You hit Mr. Duckworth when you were testing out your motor circuits," said Dr. Carson carefully. "You must never hit anyone or anything while you are testing your motors."

Chip processed the command.

"Hey, Pops, I'm home!" called a voice from upstairs.

"Come on down, Becky," said Dr. Carson. "How was your first day?"

"Great!" she answered, running down the stairs. Her wavy brown hair bounced up and down. "I think I'll like this town. How's Chip doing?"

"Well, he managed to get through his first day without anyone knowing he was an android."

"That's great!" said Becky, as she munched on an apple. "My new friend P.J. ate lunch with him and didn't think Chip was weird or anything."

"Say hi to your sister," commanded Dr. Carson.

"Hi to your sister," Chip repeated obediently.

Becky giggled. "Still a few bugs in the system?"

"It looks that way," replied Dr. Carson. "Chip had a run-in with Mr. Duckworth today. I'm afraid he'll be giving us some trouble."

"Duckworth?" said Becky. "The gym teacher? I've heard about him. They call him the Duckbrain. Everyone was talking about how someone stole his trophies! I guess he's really upset. He says he's personally going to catch the thief."

"I'm afraid he thinks Chip stole those trophies," said Dr. Carson.

"Oh, no!" cried Becky. "That could be a big problem."

"Well," said Dr. Carson, looking worried, "we'll just have to work doubly hard to keep Chip out of his way."

"I'll help you," said Becky. "I know how much this experiment means to you." She finished her apple and handed the core to the android. "Here, eat this," she said.

Chip ate the core.

"Becky! Don't do things like that," exclaimed Dr. Carson. "You know he's programmed to obey anything you tell him."

"Don't worry, Pops. I just wanted to see if he would do it. I won't mess up your experiment."

"I know you won't." Dr. Carson hugged his daughter. "I'll make dinner soon."

"Are you going to teach Chip how to wash dishes?" asked Becky.

"I think that's still your job," replied Dr. Carson. "If androids do *all* the work, people won't have anything left to do."

Becky sighed. "I wish he'd do my homework. I've got tons of geography tonight."

"It'll just seem like a ton," said Chip, echoing Jenny's remark from earlier that day.

"Very good, Chip," said Dr. Carson. "That's a good comment. Speaking of homework, do you have any for tonight?"

"Yes, Dad," answered Chip. "I have twenty-five math problems and I must read a chapter of biology."

"Biology, yuk!" said Becky, making a face. "Will he cut up frogs?"

"Probably, though I'll have to program him first. I can see I'll have to go back to school all over again," said Dr. Carson laughing. "Okay, both of you do your homework while I plan dinner."

"What's he going to eat? Nuts and bolts?" joked Becky, as she ran upstairs.

"Don't mind your sister," Dr. Carson told Chip. "She likes to make fun of everything."

"You said to follow her instructions whenever you aren't around, and minding is the same as following instructions," replied Chip.

"Yes, I guess you're right, son," said the scientist. "You're so real that I forgot for a moment and thought she might have hurt your feelings."

Chip examined his sensors. "My feelings are unhurt," he said. "All systems are okay."

"Good," responded Dr. Carson. "Now first I want you to read your biology chapter, and then do the math problems. If you have any trouble, we'll fix it after dinner."

"What's broken?" asked Chip innocently.

"Nothing," sighed his father. "Just do what I tell you and you'll be all right."

"I don't understand."

"What don't you understand?"

"How can I be all right? Half of me is left. You said so yesterday."

"Right, Chip!" said Dr. Carson sarcastically. Then quickly he added, "No, I mean, yes, half of you is right, the other half is left."

"Yes, Dad," replied Chip. "My top half is right and my bottom half is left."

Dr. Carson sighed again. "I think Becky's right. There are still a few problems with your programming."

"Becky's right? I thought she was half right and half left, like me."

"Nobody's like you, Chip!" said Dr. Carson laughing out loud. "Nobody could ever be like you."

CHAPTER 4

The next morning Chip got himself out of bed. The android had his own room, complete with posters, model airplanes, and everything a 13-year-old boy might have. Becky had even messed it up so it would look normal.

Chip unplugged his battery-charging cord from the wall and went into the kitchen to wait for everyone else. Becky, wearing her big blue sweater and short green skirt, came downstairs first and Dr. Carson followed soon after. "Good morning, Becky. Good morning, Dad," said Chip.

"Hi, Chip," said Becky. "Want some corn flakes?"

"Don't give him any," interrupted Dr. Carson. "Remember, everything he eats is just wasted. We don't have to pretend when nobody's around."

"Okay, Pops. What do you want then?" she asked her father. She rummaged through the cupboard looking for something to eat.

"Oh, anything," replied Dr. Carson, absently reading the morning paper. His glasses had slid down his nose as usual.

"Anything?" she asked. "Okay."

Becky poured out a bowl of uncooked macaroni and placed it in front of her father, who was still reading the paper. She waited.

"Oh, no!" exclaimed Dr. Carson. "There's an article in here about the trophies that were stolen from school. Chip's name is mentioned. At least they don't say he's a suspect." He put his spoon into the bowl of macaroni. "Looks like they haven't found any clues yet, but—uck! What's this?"

Becky giggled. "You said you'd eat *anything!*"

"You're a menace to society, young woman!" teased Dr. Carson.

"Sorry," giggled Becky. She brought her father a bowl of cereal.

They both laughed. Becky looked at Chip and remarked, "He's just sitting there, Pops."

"Hmmm," said Dr. Carson thoughtfully. "Chip, are you listening?"

"Yes, Dad," answered the android.

35

"Chip, when other people are laughing around you, you should laugh too."

"Order received, Dad," replied Chip. The android filed this away in his electrologic memory banks and waited patiently for something to happen.

Becky went over to Chip and put her arms around him. "He's so well behaved. Not a bit like me!" she said.

"Oh, you're not so bad," replied Dr. Carson. "But we've got to get to school or we'll be late."

The Carson family drove to school in Dr. Carson's battered green Jeep. "Chip, you must be very careful when you see Mr. Duckworth," Dr. Carson said. "Try to avoid him if you can."

"Yes, Dad," answered Chip.

Dr. Carson parked the car. Just as the bell rang, he and Becky and Chip piled out and hurried into the school.

Chip reached social studies safely that day. A gray-haired woman was sitting behind the teacher's desk. The android walked up to her and gave her a note. It was from his father and explained that yesterday Chip had not been able to find his class in time. As she read it, Chip's audio tracking program could hear the other students talking about the stolen trophies.

"Don't let it happen again," said the teacher, after she had read the note. "My name is Mrs. Crabtree, and I'm sure you'll like it here at Harbor Junior High."

"My name is Chip Carson," answered the android.

"Here's your textbook," said Mrs. Crabtree. "Now take a seat."

"Where do you want me to take it?" Chip asked, picking up an empty chair.

"Just sit down and stop wasting our time!"

Chip put the chair back down and sat in it.

"Today's subject is sugar beet production in the United States," began Mrs. Crabtree. She rose from her seat and her blue flowered dress got caught in the desk drawer. The class tried to hold back their laughter as she struggled free. Mrs. Crabtree composed herself and continued, "Who wants to guess how many tons of sugar beets are produced each year?"

A short, sandy-haired boy in front of Chip shot up his hand. "Yes, Tad?" said Mrs. Crabtree.

"Sugar beet production averages approximately thirty million tons per year," he said.

Mrs. Crabtree smiled. "Very good, Mr. Taggart. Sugar beets are an important product and—"

Chip raised his hand and the teacher called on him. "It only seems like thirty million tons," said the boy android.

"What do you mean?" said Mrs. Crabtree angrily. "It is thirty million tons or it isn't!"

The class laughed. Chip, following his father's instructions, laughed too.

"Mister Carson," snapped the teacher, "I won't have my class interrupted. Since you're such an expert on sugar beets, you can write a special report on them . . . *and turn it in tomorrow!"*

"Tough luck, kid," whispered a boy next to Chip. "We should have warned you about Old Crabby."

"Who is Old Crabby?" said Chip, without lowering his voice.

"NO TALKING!" shouted Mrs. Crabtree. The class giggled but calmed down quickly.

Strictly following instructions, Chip remained silent for the rest of the class period.

When the bell rang, the mechanical boy went quickly to his next class. On the way he processed the information he'd observed that morning. The teachers didn't want him to talk unless he raised his hand, but sometimes they got angry with what he said. This didn't fit logically with his main electrologic computer program, which told him to answer all questions if he knew the answer. Chip couldn't resolve the contradiction, so he filed it away to ask about later.

As Chip turned the corner, he spotted Mr. Duckworth up ahead. He followed his father's orders and rushed away.

The next class was math with Ms. Buzzi. Chip's father had programmed him to do the homework, and the android turned it in with the others. While Ms. Buzzi checked the answers, Chip sat down next to Jenny Driscoll.

His verbal response program told him to say "My name is Chip" only the first time he met someone, and he had a set of other greetings for further meetings. He said, "How are you today, Jenny?"

"Okay, I guess," she sighed. "I sure hated those math problems we had last night. How'd you do?"

"My father helped me," Chip answered truthfully.

"I wish I had a father like that," Jenny replied. "My dad thinks I'm supposed to learn math by magic or something. Oh, well. I guess I'll just have to face the music."

The android turned up his audio sensors and tried to pick up any sounds that were musical. Several rooms away he could hear the band practicing. "The music is in that direction," he said, pointing toward the band room.

Jenny laughed and said, "You're so funny, Chip. You're going to be great fun to have around this year."

Ms. Buzzi stood before the class holding the homework papers. "After looking over your answer sheets," she said, "I now have a good idea of how each of you will do this year. Chip Carson?"

"My name is Chip Carson," said the android.

"You have a perfect paper. Did you have algebra at the school you went to before?"

"No," answered Chip.

"Then how did you get a perfect paper?" inquired Ms. Buzzi. "I deliberately gave some problems that were too hard for the class."

"My father helped me," replied Chip.

"Dummy!" whispered Jenny. "Don't tell her *that!*"

Ms. Buzzi smiled like a cat about to eat a mouse. "Well, then, you can do double homework tonight, and you must do it yourself. Your father can't help you."

"My father always helps me," said Chip. His programming was having trouble with Ms. Buzzi's last statement. How could he not ask his father for help? That was one of his principal rules. But Dr. Carson had also told him to obey all teachers.

"I'll tell him not to. You'll never learn if he does your homework!" answered Ms. Buzzi.

Chip's electrologic program was almost short-circuiting! One of his primary functions was to learn, but how *could* he learn if he didn't ask his father? "I don't understand," said the android.

"Never mind," snapped Ms. Buzzi. "I'll explain it to your father, and he can make you understand. We've got to start class now." With that she began the lesson.

40

When math was over, Chip met Jenny Driscoll and her friends for lunch again. As he was sitting down, he overheard a girl at the next table say, "I hear Mr. Duckworth has a suspect in the robbery."

"Oh, really?" replied her friend. "Well, if I know Duckworth, he'll pound the truth out of whoever stole those trophies."

"Listen, Chip," the android heard Jenny say. "You shouldn't have told Ms. Buzzi that your father did your homework."

"Why not?" asked Chip innocently. "I'm supposed to answer all questions truthfully."

"Not to teachers!" said P.J.

"That's right," added Mario. "Anything you say will be held against you."

"Hey, Erin," said Scott, but before she could answer, Alex, who was sitting on her other side, pushed her into Scott.

"Quit it!" shouted Erin.

Alex laughed. "But Erin," he began, "Scott said your name, and anything he says will be held against him. I was just helping out!"

"You are definitely weird," said Erin good-naturedly. She pushed Scott away. He crashed into Chip, who bumped into the boy sitting next to him, wearing a black leather jacket and a short spiked haircut.

The boy shoved back *hard!* "Watch it, punk!" he said.

41

"Watch what?" answered Chip.

The boy made a fist and shook it in Chip's face. "Watch this knock your head off."

"How could I watch that? My eyes are in my head," said Chip.

"Cool it, Chip, he means business," said Scott. He pulled Chip back to his seat.

Before Chip could ask what business the boy was in, the bell rang and everybody jumped up. Jenny and her friends hustled Chip away before anything else happened. When they reached the hall, Scott said, "Stay away from him, Chip. That's Jake Blocker. He's big trouble. Don't get in a fight with him!"

"Yeah, he was almost kicked out of school for fighting last year," said Erin.

"How could he fight against a year?" asked Chip. "Only people can fight."

"Isn't Chip a riot!" shouted P.J.

"I thought you didn't want me to fight," said Chip, confused. "Shouldn't I stay out of riots, too?"

"Well, the teachers will riot if we don't get to class," said Jenny. "See you later, Chip."

"Goodbye," he replied.

From behind him, Erin called, "Hey, Chip, slow down!"

The android immediately turned his synchronized sector motor control to low speed and began to move very slowly down the hall. His arms and legs seemed to float up and down as

42

he walked along at a snail's pace. Erin laughed when she saw what he was doing. The other students pushed their way past him, rushing to their classes. Two boys in varsity jackets snickered and pointed at Chip as he slowly strolled toward them.

Erin ran up to him. "Thanks for letting me catch up," she said, "but if you don't move faster, you're going to be trampled to death."

Chip's dynakinetic logic program concluded that going slow was dangerous, so he turned his motor control up all the way and ran forward at top speed. Three girls leaped out of his way as he plunged down the hall.

"Stop, Chip!" cried Erin.

The android immediately halted his sector motors and almost lost his balance as he jolted to a stop. Erin burst out laughing. "You're so funny, Chip!"

Chip's verbal response program determined that this statement was a compliment, so he replied, "Thank you."

"I bet you'd be the life of the party," said Erin.

"Then it wouldn't be much of a party," Chip remarked.

"Why not?"

"If I were the life of the party, what would have happened to everyone else? Would they be dead?"

"Compared to you they would be!"

"That's too bad," Chip replied.

"You're telling me! I thought this was going to be another dull year in boring old Harbor City until you showed up." Approaching the door of Mr. Diller's English class, Erin added, "I'm glad I got a chance to know you a little better. I liked walking to class with you. Maybe we could do it more often?"

"I only have English scheduled once a day," Chip explained. "So I don't think I should come here more often than that."

Erin laughed. "You're right," she said. "English class once a day is often enough for me."

The bell rang and Chip and Erin quickly took their seats.

When class was over, Chip went straight to study hall, following his schedule properly. Since he was not programmed to study without his father helping him, the android pretended to read one of his textbooks, flipping the pages at the same rate as the students around him.

After study hall came biology, where the teacher announced that, yes, they would cut up frogs. Everybody except Chip groaned. Finally the school day was over. The android had successfully avoided Mr. Duckworth each time he saw him.

Becky was nowhere in sight, so Chip started walking home alone. He had gone two blocks when Jake Blocker jumped out from behind a fence and snarled, "Okay, kid. You didn't think

44

I was going to let you get away with shoving me at lunch, did you?"

"I didn't shove you," answered Chip. "Do you want me to shove you?"

Jake made a fist and swung at Chip. The android instantly recognized this as an attack and remembered Scott's words about avoiding a fight. The synchronized sector motors in his arms and legs easily moved his mechanical body out of the way before the bully could hit him.

Jake's fist whizzed past Chip's head and he almost lost his balance. Surprised, Jake said, "How'dja do that?"

The android was not allowed to reveal his secret identity, so he gave one of the answers his father had told him to use when asked such questions. "I just did it," he said.

"Let's see you do it again," Jake dared him. He raised both hands and leaped for Chip.

Again the android ducked out of the way. This time Jake lost his balance and sprawled on the pavement. "I'm going to murder you, you dog!" he yelled.

"I am not a dog," replied Chip. "Dogs have four legs and I have only two."

"Well, I'm going to break both of 'em before I'm through," said Jake, scrambling to his feet. He lunged for the android's legs but Chip darted to the left with a quick thrust of his motors.

"How can you do that?" asked Jake again.

"I just lifted up my legs and put them down two feet six inches away," answered the android.

"Shut your mouth," cried Jake. "I'm going to plaster you all over the sidewalk!"

Chip snapped his mouth shut with a loud click. However, the android's speech came from a tiny speaker hidden in his throat. "I have to get home soon," he said, his mouth still closed.

"So you're a ventriloquist too!" cried Jake. He drew his fist back for another blow.

Before Jake could attack, several kids ran up the sidewalk. Becky was among them, and so were P.J. and Alex.

"Come on, Chip," said Becky. "You've got to get home."

Jake edged back. "You haven't seen the last of me, punk," he said.

Becky and her friends pulled Chip away. "You'd better be careful, Chip," P.J. said. "If we hadn't come in time, he might have hurt you."

"I think my brother can handle himself," replied Becky proudly. To Chip she said, "Did he hit you?"

"No. I moved out of the way," answered Chip.

"Yeah," said Alex. "I saw you ducking and dodging. Maybe you should try out for the football team."

"I've got to study," said Chip. His program told him to say this if any after-school or team activities were mentioned.

"Don't remind me," groaned Alex.

Chip and Becky arrived at their house and said goodbye to their friends. Becky pulled her brother inside. "Come on, Chip, I want to see how fast you can do the dishes. And don't tell Pops!"

"Why shouldn't I tell him how fast I did the dishes?" asked Chip.

"Because . . . oh, just because I say so. Don't mention dishes to him at all, and that's an order," replied Becky.

"I must obey orders from you or Dad," answered the android dutifully.

Becky pushed him in front of the sink. "Right!" she said. "Now get to work while I watch TV."

CHAPTER 5

The next morning went smoothly for Chip. Unfortunately, lunch didn't go well at all. When the android arrived at the cafeteria, everything was in chaos.

Kids were handed bag lunches instead of hot meals, and lots of the students were angry. Chip got his bag and carried it over to Jenny and her friends.

"Isn't this awful?" said Jenny. "No hot lunches for a week!"

"What happens in a week?" asked Chip, opening up his bag. Inside were two soggy tuna sandwiches, a carton of milk, and an apple.

"That's when they'll get the ovens fixed," said P.J. with a sigh. "Some creep broke a window, snuck into the cafeteria last night, and

48

turned on one of the ovens," she added. "There was a fire and everything's a big mess."

Mario pulled out his sandwiches and exclaimed, "Peanut butter, ick! Anybody want to trade? How about you, Chip?"

"Trade a U for what?" asked Chip.

Erin laughed. "Oh, Chip, I love your sense of humor. We need to see more of that around here."

"I think you'd just like to see more of *Chip* around here," muttered Mario.

Erin glared at Mario. "I know for a fact that I could stand to see and *hear* less of you. Grumble, grumble, grumble—that's all you ever do."

At that moment the android's sensors alerted him that a hand was on his shoulder. In fact, his memory program told him that he had experienced the same kind of pressure only a few days ago.

It was Mr. Duckworth. "Principal Gutman wants to see you," he said. "Come along quietly."

Chip got up and walked silently beside the gym teacher, still holding his lunch bag. When they reached the principal's office, Mr. Duckworth told Chip to sit in a chair and wait.

While the android sat and waited, he called his father on his internal interface radio. "Dad, Mr. Duckworth brought me to the principal's office. What should I do?"

The response came back a moment later, but

49

it wasn't what Chip's program expected. Dr. Carson's voice said, "I'm on a short field trip with my class, Chip. Answer all questions and use your electrologic index of conflict resolution principles. This is a recording."

Chip didn't have long to wait. Mr. Duckworth came back a moment later and led him into the principal's office. "This is the boy I told you about," he said.

"Hello, Chip," said the short, overweight man behind the desk. "We want to ask you some questions."

"My name is Chip Carson," said the android helpfully.

"Yes, I know," began the principal. "What were you doing yesterday after school?"

The android examined his memory banks and said, "I did the dishes for my sister." Becky had told him not to tell his father, but she hadn't told him not to tell anyone else.

"Be more direct," said Mr. Duckworth. "This kid isn't exactly on the ball."

"Mr. Duckworth," Mr. Gutman said with a trace of annoyance in his voice, "please watch what you say about our students while they're in the room." He turned back to Chip. "Were you home all evening?" he asked kindly.

"Yes," answered Chip.

"Was anybody else at home?"

"My sister Becky."

"What about your parents?"

Chip said, "My father was home for dinner. Then he went out with Becky to the grocery store."

"Ha!" said the gym teacher. "I told you so!"

"Take it easy, Mr. Duckworth," cautioned the principal. To the android, he said, "Do you know why you've been called in here?"

"No," answered Chip.

"Can you guess?" replied Principal Gutman.

The android had a program called *Guess*. It had been an early game that his father had programmed into him to test out his logic circuits. Chip said, "I'm thinking of a number between one and ten. Can you guess it?"

"Five," said the principal without thinking.

"Too high," replied Chip. "Guess again."

"Wait a minute," cried Mr. Duckworth. "What's this got to do with the fire?"

"Now, Chip," said Mr. Gutman, "please pay attention."

"The answer was three," said Chip, still operating from his father's game program. "Do you want to guess another number?"

"NO!" shouted the principal. "I want some answers about the cafeteria fire. What do you know about it?"

"Some creep broke a window, snuck into the cafeteria last night, and turned on one of the ovens. There was a fire and everything's a big mess," answered Chip. He used his audio record-and-replay circuit to recall P.J.'s words

51

about the fire; unfortunately he also used P.J.'s voice.

"Young man, I've had just about enough out of you!" fumed the principal.

"Does that mean I can go?" asked Chip. "My English class starts in seven minutes and thirty-two seconds."

"No, you can't go," said Mr. Gutman, barely able to hold his temper. "If you were innocent, you'd give me a straight answer."

Chip activated his conflict-resolution program. He knew what innocent meant, and he assumed he'd been giving straight answers. However, his electrologic program told him that if something wasn't working, he ought to try the opposite.

"Did you set the fire?" said Mr. Duckworth.

"Yes," said Chip, trying a different approach.

"I knew it!" yelled the gym teacher triumphantly. "Call the cops."

"Let's be sure of this," said the principal hesitantly. Turning to Chip, he asked, "Now, why did you set the fire?"

"My father asked me to," answered Chip.

"What!" exclaimed Mr. Duckworth. "Your father's the new science teacher!"

"You didn't tell me this is Dr. Carson's son," the principal said to Mr. Duckworth. "Not that it makes any difference. But this is a serious charge, Chip."

"Oh," said Chip. "Do you need some electricity? There's a wall socket behind you where you can get a charge."

"Don't try to get funny with me!" threatened Mr. Gutman. Then he calmed himself down and said, "Let's get back to your father."

"He's on a field trip," responded Chip. "Do you want to join him?"

"No thanks," said the principal sarcastically. "Now, Chip, tell me *why* your father wanted you to set the fire."

"So the house would be nice and warm when he got back," said the android.

"The house? What about the cafeteria?" said Mr. Duckworth.

"Do you want me to show you where it is? I can take you there," answered Chip.

"Wait a minute!" said Mr. Gutman. "Where did you set the fire?"

"In the fireplace in our living room," replied the boy android.

Mr. Gutman sighed and buried his head in his hands.

"This is getting us nowhere," he said. "Mr. Duckworth, we don't have enough proof to hold this boy any longer. What do you suggest?"

Mr. Duckworth whispered something in Mr. Gutman's ear. Chip turned up his auditory sensors so he could hear him. "Because he's

53

new in town," said Mr. Duckworth, "I think we should have one of the students look after him."

"Good idea," replied the principal. Smiling, he turned to Chip and said, "Since you're new at Harbor Junior High, I think we should have a student help you get around."

"I don't think another student can carry me," said the android.

"You just need a new friend," answered Mr. Gutman, straining to be polite.

"Good!" replied Chip. "My father wants me to make friends."

The principal then told Chip to report back to his office instead of going to study hall that afternoon. Chip left and hurried to his English class. He was late, but when he explained to his teacher that he had been in the principal's office, Mr. Diller nodded and told him to sit down.

As Chip walked by Erin, she smiled and waved. "I was wondering what happened to you," she whispered.

The android didn't answer. He sat down in his seat next to Alex. "What did Gutbelly have to say?" Alex asked.

"He wanted to know about the fire in the cafeteria," answered Chip.

"NO TALKING!" shouted Mr. Diller.

Alex whispered back, "Chip, you should whisper or he'll get you for sure."

The android's voice circuits were not able to whisper, but he could make a hissing sound by running his jaw motors at high speed. So he started to hiss.

"QUIET!" yelled Mr. Diller to the class. Then turning to Chip, he said, "Are you talking, Carson?"

The android hissed again. The class laughed, and Chip laughed along with them, still hissing.

"*Mister* Carson!" yelled the English teacher. "Will you please speak normally or I'll send you right *back* to the principal's office."

"I have to be there in forty-five minutes and seventeen seconds," said Chip, consulting his internal clock.

"Maybe you should go now," said Mr. Diller coldly.

"You're going to get it," whispered Alex. "Sorry, kid!"

"What will I get?" asked the mechanical boy.

"That's it!" shouted the teacher. "Go to the principal's office now and tell him you were thrown out of my class for talking."

Chip stood up and waited.

"Well?" said Mr. Diller.

"Aren't you going to throw me?" asked Chip.

"Do you think you can manage to get there by yourself?" snapped Mr. Diller.

"Yes."

"THEN GO NOW!"

Chip headed straight for the principal's office. He opened the door without knocking and walked right in.

"Hey!" exclaimed Mr. Gutman. He shoved a magazine into his desk. "You're not supposed to be here for an hour."

"Mr. Diller sent me," replied the android. "He was going to throw me out, but changed his mind."

"Then why did he send you here?"

"For talking," said Chip. "I was trying to whisper but I couldn't do it."

"Terrific!" said Principal Gutman sarcastically. "Now wait outside the door and don't make a move until I call you."

Chip left the office and stood directly in front of the door. He turned off most of his motor circuits and waited.

At 12:55, the bell rang. The door opened and Mr. Gutman crashed directly into Chip. Since Chip's gyroscopes were turned off, he fell over on his face.

Mr. Gutman tumbled down on top of him. He scrambled to his feet, but the android remained on the floor, still waiting. "Are you all right?" asked the principal. "Why don't you get up?"

"I am only half right," said Chip. "Do you want me to get up or should I wait longer?"

"Get up before the school board comes in

56

here and wonders why my students are sleeping on the floor," he ordered.

Chip stood up. "I only sleep at night," he said.

While Mr. Gutman tried to think of a reply, another student came into the office. "You wanted to see me, sir?" he said.

"Yes, Taggart. Come into my office. Chip, you wait out here—but sit down this time."

Chip sat down on the floor.

"CARSON!" roared the principal. "Sit in a chair!"

Chip got up and moved to a chair while Tad Taggart and Mr. Gutman went into the office.

When they came out a few minutes later, the principal said, "Chip, this is Tad Taggart. He'll help you get adjusted to school. I hope you'll be friends."

Tad held out his hand. "Hi," he said.

Chip had a program which told him about shaking hands. He reached out and gripped Tad's hand. Unfortunately, the program hadn't been tested yet. He squeezed Tad's hand a little too hard.

"Ow!" yelled Tad. He pulled his hand away. "Watch it!"

Chip looked at the boy's hand intently.

The principal was holding a slip of paper. He gave it to Chip and said, "I'm transferring you out of study hall. I want you to work with Tad in the computer lab during that hour. He'll help you learn all about computers, won't you, Tad?"

"Sure," replied Tad, still nursing his crushed hand. "Maybe he can type for me, since I may never be able to use this hand again."

Mr. Gutman tried to smile. "Well, run along, I've got work to do," he said. "Remember what I told you, Taggart."

Chip ran out of the room. Tad followed him. He caught up with him halfway down the hall. "Wait! You're going the wrong way!" he shouted.

"He told me to run," said Chip. "And my father told me to obey all teachers."

"He meant that we were supposed to leave. 'Run along' is another way to say that," said Tad. He steered the android toward the computer lab.

When they got there, Chip scanned the room. Being familiar with his father's computers, he recognized that most of the lab's cubicles contained terminals which were probably hooked up to a large mainframe computer somewhere else. He also saw a portable desktop microcomputer, similar to the one his father had at home. Several kids were clustered around it, playing a game. "I'm in charge of the computer lab during this period," Tad said. "You can help me."

58

"I like to help people," said Chip, using one of his stock responses.

"Good," said the boy. He handed Chip a pile of printouts and sat him down at one of the terminals. "One of those dopey kids erased a file yesterday. You can type in these programs while I work on a spare memory board for our microcomputer. Don't bother me until you've finished," replied Tad.

Chip began to type.

Five minutes later he walked over to Tad, who was busy soldering wires. "Tired already?" Tad said.

"I've typed in the programs you gave me," responded Chip.

"Gutbelly warned me about you, but I didn't think you'd lie about such an obvious thing," said Taggart, irritated.

Chip checked his gyroscope. Then he said, "I'm standing up, not lying."

Tad grimaced, then put the soldering iron down and went over to Chip's terminal. He punched a few keys and examined the program on the screen. "How could he type that fast?" he wondered. "Probably full of mistakes, though."

While the program began to load, Tad turned to Chip and said, "It'll be a couple of minutes before all the data is calculated and the game is ready to play. That's the one thing I can't stand about computers. It drives me crazy that some programs take so long to boot up on the screen. I hate to wait. When my dad came to visit me last summer, he tried to teach me how to play golf, but all that standing around waiting was dull, boring, and stupid! I like fast action video games a lot better. You should see me play down at Tom's video arcade. They call me the Arcade King."

Just then the word READY printed across the monitor, indicating that the program had loaded correctly and the game was ready to play.

Tad pressed the fire button on the joystick. A blue cartoon character raced across the screen and Tad guided it through a complicated maze, avoiding the whirling red tornado that was trying to engulf everything.

"Pretty good game, huh?" he said with pride.

"Yes," replied Chip, watching the screen. "It reminds me of one that my dad has."

"Mine is better!" snapped Tad, switching off the game. "Are you sure you typed all of this? It still seems hard to believe."

"I'm sure," the android answered, checking his memory banks. "I typed everything you gave me."

"Okay, Chip, I guess you weren't lying, but I didn't know anybody could type that fast. Have you worked on computers before?"

"Yes," answered Chip. "My father has a computer in the basement."

"Well, why didn't you say you were a fellow hacker? That calls for a handshake," he exclaimed, extending his hand, but he yanked it back before Chip could shake it again. "I forgot about your Vulcan death grip!"

Chip also pulled his hand back, but he threw himself off balance. His gyroscopes tried to compensate, but he fell against the lab bench and his hand came down on the hot soldering iron! Chip's sensor circuits detected the heat, but by the time he removed his hand, a small piece of plastic skin had burned away.

"Hey, watch out! That soldering iron's hot!" yelled Tad.

Chip had an internal program labeled *self-preservation*. It told him never to reveal to anyone that he was not a human being. His logic told him that his skin now did not look "normal" and that Tad must not see it. He turned his hand so that the burned part was facing his body.

"You all right?" said Tad.

"I'm only half right," responded Chip, keeping his hand covered.

Tad picked up the soldering iron and examined it closely. "What's this sticky plastic stuff on the tip?" he muttered. "I thought it was clean."

"What should I do now?" asked Chip.

Still puzzling over the plastic on his soldering iron, Tad handed Chip another pile of printouts and said, "Type these. And why don't you meet me here after school? We can walk home together, okay?"

Dr. Carson had given specific orders that the android wasn't to walk home with other kids. "I walk home by myself," Chip replied.

"Come on, we're friends now, aren't we?" said Tad. "I'll be looking for you after school!" He smiled and went back to the lab bench.

The android took the printouts and sat down at his own terminal. He scanned the room quickly, determined that no one was looking at him, and examined the damaged spot on his skin. Gray steel poked through the burned plastic. If anyone saw it, they might suspect that Chip was not quite human!

CHAPTER 6

When the bell rang, Chip started toward biology, his last class of the day. As he passed through the halls, he took care to shield his burned hand.

Suddenly he heard a familiar voice behind him. "Hi, Chip. How's it going?" said Becky.

Making sure that no one else could hear, the android said, "I burned my hand. What should I do?"

Becky examined the mechanical hand. "That looks nasty," she said. "You should put a Band-Aid on it. I've got one in my purse. Pops can fix it better when you get home tonight."

She carefully bandaged her brother's hand. "Don't worry," she said, "things will be all

63

right. With this Band-Aid covering the damage, no one will discover your secret."

"I'm not programmed to worry," said Chip.

Becky giggled. "Are you programmed to say thank you?"

"If someone gives me something. You gave me a Band-Aid, so I should thank you. Thank you, Becky."

"Don't mention it," she replied. "I'll be a little bit late tonight, but don't tell Dad. He won't get home until after dinner. I'm going over to P.J.'s house. How are you getting along?"

"I've got a new friend named Tad Taggart," replied Chip. "He wants me to meet him after school."

Becky thought for a moment and then she said, "I don't think Dad would like you to do that yet. I think you should go straight home. Your programs still have a few bugs in them."

"There are no insects inside my body," replied the android. "My surfaces are completely enclosed with high-resolution, multiflex plastic skin."

"Maybe they crawled in through the hole in your hand before I bandaged it," grinned Becky.

"What should I do?" asked Chip.

"Go home and vacuum all the carpets," said Becky, testing Chip to see how much she could get away with.

64

"Should I go home now or finish my last class first?" he inquired.

Becky hugged her brother. "Oh, Chip!" she said. "You're so silly, but I like you. Finish your class first."

"Okay," replied the mechanical boy. "Thank you."

"What for?"

"For giving me a hug. That is a gift, isn't it?"

"You bet. Now go on to your last class or we'll both be late."

Chip went straight to biology. For once he wasn't late. He took his seat at a table with three other kids. The teacher hadn't arrived yet, so one of the kids asked, "Who knows a good joke?"

"What's green and dangerous?" said a curly-haired boy.

"Everybody knows that one, Sid," replied a girl named Stephanie. "A frog with a machine gun."

"Please don't mention frogs!" said another boy, Mark, who was drawing in his notebook. "They're so gross. I can't believe we have to cut them up."

"What else is green and—"

"Shhh, here comes Quacky," whispered Stephanie.

Mrs. Quackenbush entered the room, holding up a potted plant. "Good afternoon, class. Who knows what this is?"

"It's a Martian in a hot tub!" somebody called out.

"No," replied the teacher cheerfully. "This is a radish plant. We're all going to grow radishes and study them." She began to hand out radish seeds. "Plant them in the pots by the window and keep good records," she said.

"That's your department, Mark!" said Stephanie. "You keep the records."

"I guess I can manage that," he replied. "But when we dissect frogs, you'll have to do the cutting!"

"Not me!" she exclaimed. They began poking the radish seeds into dirt-filled pots. Mark wrote down how many seeds were in each pot.

"These seeds remind me of the raisins at lunch today," said Sid. "Disgusting!"

"Don't remind me," replied Stephanie. "I'll be glad when they get the ovens fixed. I wonder if whoever ruined the ovens was the same person who stole the school trophies? What do you think, Chip?"

"I don't know," answered the android. "I wasn't there."

"Of course you weren't," said Stephanie. "We heard that the Duckbrain is trying to frame you, but we know you're innocent."

"Why would he want to frame me?" asked the android. "I'm not a window."

"You're not a door, either, Chip," interrupted Mark. "Move over, I can't see how many seeds you're planting."

"Twenty-seven," counted Chip. "I'm through."

The students stood back and looked at the tiny pots filled with dirt. "I sure hope that the guy who stole the trophies doesn't steal our radishes," commented Sid.

"Me, too," added Mark. "Not after all this hard work."

"Hard work, hah!" replied Stephanie. "And what makes you think the trophy thief is a guy? Maybe a girl—" The bell rang and the rest of the class ran out of the room before she could finish.

Chip walked through the crowded corridor to his locker. Consulting his memory banks, the android decided he should go directly home. According to his internal data directory of Carson's laws, Becky's orders outweighed Tad Taggart's request to meet him at the computer lab.

As the android selected the necessary books for the night's homework, Erin walked up behind him. "Hi, Chip! I've been meaning to tell you—that's a nice sweater you're wearing. It matches the color of your eyes."

"Thank you," he replied, closing the locker door.

"You know, Chip, I sure am glad you moved here."

"Why?" he asked.

"Because you're so much fun to be around. I'd like to see more of you."

"Which parts?" asked Chip, examining his body.

Erin turned red with embarrassment. "All of you," she said.

"I'll have to ask my dad if you want to see all of me."

"Don't you dare!" shrieked Erin. "Chip Carson, sometimes I can't believe the things you say."

"Everything I say is one hundred percent true," he explained.

"You can't be serious," said Erin.

"That's correct. I'm not Serious, I'm Chip."

Erin rolled her eyes and shook her head. She quickly changed the subject, asking, "Have you made a lot of new friends since you moved here?"

Chip quickly counted the people he'd met and his verbal response program determined that this was a lot. "Yes, I've made a lot of friends."

"Do you have a girlfriend?" Erin asked.

"You're a girl and you're my friend. Does that make you my girlfriend?" the android asked.

Erin blushed and giggled. "Not yet, but maybe we could talk more about that. Do you want to go over to the Burger Bear and have a Coke with me?"

Chip's electrologic memory banks recalled that his father had told him to go straight home, so he answered, "I can't. I have to go home now."

"Okay," said Erin with a disappointed frown. "Maybe another day. Well, I gotta run. I'll see you tomorrow in art class. Bye!"

Chip waved as she hurried down the hall. Then he threw his book bag over his shoulder and headed home.

While crossing the street, Chip received an error signal from his left leg. *Something was wrong with the motor!* He tried to step up onto the curb but the motor whirred at high speed. His right leg was still moving, though, so the android spun around and walked back into the traffic.

An ice cream truck screeched to a halt, narrowly avoiding Chip. "Watch it!" yelled the driver.

"Watch what?" replied Chip, trying to get his leg motor back to normal. Even though he was standing still, his leg kept hopping in the air.

The driver honked his horn, backed up, and zoomed around him. Chip reached down, twisted his leg to the right, and commanded the leg to walk. Now the left leg moved, but twice as fast as the right leg! Chip was going around in

69

circles. The traffic was stopped in both directions. The android's main program warned him that this extra activity was putting a strain on his microbatteries.

Dozens of horns were honking as the mechanical boy tried a new approach. He turned up the speed on his right leg. Instantly he was propelled across the street and down the sidewalk. Chip stopped when he was a block away. He did a self-test on the left leg and began in-circuit changes to readjust the voltages to the synchronized leg motors.

His cybernetic voltage regulator reported that all motor control circuits were now balanced. He walked a few feet and saw that everything was normal. Everything, that is, except his battery power. Chip carefully measured the number of steps it would take to get home and the amount of energy left in his battery reserve. Just enough, he calculated.

The android walked another block. His tracking sensors showed him that two boys were obstructing the sidewalk ahead. They were pushing each other and moving around in a way that Chip determined would require extra energy to get past them. The android prepared to cross the street and avoid the dangerous encounter.

But as he got nearer to the two boys, his visual pattern-recognition program told him that the little one was Tad Taggart and the one in the black T-shirt was Jake Blocker. His object detection program concluded they were fighting.

Activating his logic program, Chip tried to decide what to do. *Tad was a "friend" and Jake was not a "friend." His father had told him to help friends. Therefore, Tad needed help.* Chip walked forward.

"Hey, here's another punk kid!" shouted Jake. "This is my lucky day!" He shoved Tad to the ground.

"Go for help!" yelled Tad. "Jake's beating me up."

The android checked his battery levels. They had not gone up, and he had no extra energy. Not for anything. He walked up to Jake Blocker. In the few short days since Chip had been at school, he'd seen several fights. The android could have fought, but his internal directory strictly ordered him never to injure a human being.

"This time I'm going to knock your head off," said Jake, raising his fist at the mechanical boy.

Chip had no extra energy for fighting. Even dodging Jake's fists might use up his batteries just enough so that he couldn't get home. If he ran out of energy in the middle of the sidewalk, people would learn that he was an android.

"Hit him, Chip," said Tad, trying to get up off the ground. His lip was bleeding.

Instead, Jake raised *his* arm and swung at Chip. The android did nothing. His logic circuits were working at full tilt, but they couldn't help him resolve the contradictions.

Jake's fist crashed into Chip's metal chin. "Yeeoww!" he yelled. "My hand!!"

While Jake nursed his sore hand, Tad struggled to his feet. "Let's get out of here!" he cried.

"I have to go straight home," answered Chip.

Tad raced down the sidewalk but the android had only enough energy to walk. Jake Blocker took off after Chip yelling, "What did you do to my hand, you little creep?"

Chip swiveled his head around. "I didn't do anything," he said. "You struck me."

"You hurt me!" howled Jake.

This caused Chip's logic program to go into overdrive. He had violated one of his prime orders! "Are you injured?" asked Chip, wanting to make sure.

"Who, me?" said Jake, shaking his hand. "Nothing hurts me for long," he barked. "But now I'm angry!"

Risking some precious battery power, Chip speeded up his sector motors to escape. But Jake leaped forward and tackled the android's legs.

Chip went down hard. Tad raced back to help. He kicked Jake Blocker with all his strength, and then ran away down the street.

"I'll get you later," yelled Jake as he got up.

Jake decided Tad wasn't worth running after. He turned back to Chip. "I'll say one thing for you. You're not yellow like that Taggart kid. He's halfway home by now!"

"He's not yellow," replied the android. "His skin is pink and his hair is light brown."

Jake stood over Chip with his hands on his hips and an angry scowl on his face. "Get up, punk, so I can knock you down again."

Chip's logic program told him that this didn't compute. "Wouldn't I save energy by staying on the ground?"

Jake laughed. "I guess you would, you little runt. And I'll probably save myself a broken hand if I let you go home this time. I'll beat you up tomorrow!"

"Then I can get up now," said the android. Unfortunately, Chip's batteries were too low for him to operate his gyroscope, his arms, and his legs at the same time. He tried to get up, but he stumbled over and crashed to the ground.

"Hey, are you okay?" Jake asked. For the first time, he sounded worried.

"No," said the android. "I can't get up."

Jake knelt down and Chip rested his hand lightly against the larger boy's shoulder as he got up. Even so, Jake exclaimed, "Whew! I must have worn myself out knocking you two guys around. It feels like you weigh a ton."

"It only seems like a ton," said Chip as he

staggered to his feet. Making a quick assessment of his C-13 microbatteries, the android determined that if he switched off most of his auxiliary circuits, he could cover the remaining distance.

"I didn't hurt you, did I?" asked Jake.

"No, I'm fine," answered the android, walking away.

"Good!" he exclaimed. "I like a kid who can take it."

"Take what?" Chip called over his shoulder.

"Take *this!*" Jake kicked the android's leg. "Yeeouch!" he shouted as his toes slammed into Chip's steel body. "I must be getting weak in my old age," Jake muttered as he limped away.

Chip moved steadily toward home. He staggered up the front steps and with his last remaining bit of energy, opened the door, went into his room, and plugged himself in.

CHAPTER 7

Becky arrived home later. She pulled off her oversized pink sweater and threw her book bag onto the couch. Then she noticed the carpet hadn't been vacuumed. Since Chip was programmed to follow her orders, she instantly knew something was wrong. She raced to the android's bedroom and found him sprawled across the floor.

"Wake up, Chip!" she yelled.

The android didn't move. A power cord ran from his leg to the wall socket. "I know you're only an android," said Becky, "but I'm really worried about you."

She inspected the cord and socket, but everything seemed plugged in correctly. Had the android short-circuited? Becky remembered her father mentioning a master reset switch inside the mechanical boy's ear. But which ear?

Becky took a pencil from Chip's desk and probed gently in his right ear. *Eeeeeeeeee!* An electronic screech filled the room. She yanked the pencil out.

Cautiously she pushed it into Chip's left ear. *Click!* The android opened his eyes. Becky jumped back as Chip rose to his feet and began testing his synchronized sector motors. First one arm shot out, then the other. The android's right knee lifted, and kicked out. Standing on one foot, his internal gyroscope holding him steady, Chip twirled around six times. Then he shifted onto the other foot and repeated the motions.

When he finished, Becky asked, "What happened? Are you okay?"

"My batteries ran down on the way home from school," answered the android. "This was caused by a problem in the motors of my left leg."

"You've got a tough life, Chip," said Becky. "Your hand's burned, your leg motors are goofed up, and you've got a pencil sticking out of your ear!"

Chip reached up and felt around his head with the cybernetic digisensors in his fingertips. He found the pencil and tried to remove it. Unfortunately, he pushed it in and—*click!*—turned himself off again.

Becky shook her head as her brother fell to the floor. Then she reached down, pushed the pencil in, and clicked on the reset switch. This time she pulled the pencil out herself.

As Chip started his exercises again, Becky said, "Since your leg motors are out of whack, I guess I'll have to vacuum myself."

"Are you wearing a carpet?" asked Chip. "Only carpets need to be vacuumed."

Becky laughed and said, "Maybe that would be a good idea! Instead of washing my clothes, I could just vacuum them. But for now, I want you to wait in your room until Pops gets home."

Dr. Carson was very tired when he came in the door a short time later. His brown tweed jacket was rumpled and his tie was undone. He dumped a huge pile of papers on the cluttered coffee table and flopped onto the couch. Becky felt sorry for him, but she had to tell him about Chip's mechanical problem.

Dr. Carson sighed and silently took Chip down to the basement. Dismantling a synchronized sector motor was the kind of job that would normally take a few days, but it would have to be done tonight.

The scientist commanded his creation to climb up on the lab bench. When Chip's legs were in a good position, Dr. Carson deactivated the android. He popped open an access hatch in Chip's left thigh and removed the gleaming motor.

"In order to get more time for these repairs," he mumbled, "I'd risk telling the school you were sick, but the school nurse might ask to examine you." Dr. Carson hooked the motor up to an oscilloscope and turned it on. While the motor whirred, he adjusted the synchronized magnetos back and forth. After several hours he finally got a stable power wave image on the oscilloscope screen.

Dr. Carson put the delicate motor back into its leg cavity and switched the android on again. Then he ordered Chip to walk around the crowded basement, following a line painted on the floor.

"Okay, Dad," said Chip. He began walking, but he veered to the left and crashed into a huge radar dish. "The right motor went too fast," reported the android.

Once again, Dr. Carson deactivated his creation and went through the whole process, this time with the motor in the right leg, so that the two motors would be perfectly synchronized. When he reactivated the android, Chip was able to follow the line perfectly, successfully weaving his way past the boxes of electronic equipment Dr. Carson had collected from garage sales, phone company auctions, and military surplus outlets.

Next Dr. Carson transferred the data in Chip's memory banks to the master computer.

Examining the day's events, the scientist was dismayed when he learned of the fight with Jake. "This is terrible," he muttered. "Now *two* people are after you. This Jake person and Mr. Duckworth."

At that moment, Becky ran down the stairs, her short blue skirt swinging behind her. She handed her father a plate of cookies and a glass of milk.

"What's in them this time—sawdust?" he said, picking up a cookie suspiciously.

"No, Pops, these are real cookies," Becky answered with a grin. "You looked so tired when you came home that I thought I'd bake you your favorite kind, chocolate chip."

"Yes?" said the android.

"Not you, silly!" said Becky. "You're not made of chocolate!"

"My name is Chip," said the mechanical boy.

"And if you were covered with chocolate, you'd be a chocolate chip," replied Becky.

"Then I am a high-resolution, multiflex plastic chip," answered the android, "because that's what I'm covered with now."

"Good logic, Chip," said Dr. Carson.

"My logic chips are good," said the android, running a short test of his electrologic circuit chips to make sure.

Becky nibbled on a cookie and asked, "Will he really be okay?"

Dr. Carson stopped the android and looked at a printout of Chip's walking abilities. "I think so, but his mechanical difficulties aren't nearly as much of a problem as Mr. Duckworth is. I'm afraid he may be able to convince Mr. Gutman that Chip's the one responsible for the outbreak of vandalism at the school."

"But he's innocent. You could prove it by playing Chip's tapes," declared Becky.

"And ruin my work completely!" replied the scientist. "This experiment can only succeed if nobody knows that my android is not a real boy. I've worked so hard to make Chip a success. I'd really hate to have him fail because someone vandalized the school."

"Don't worry, Pops. Chip's a winner if ever there was one," said Becky, patting the android on the head. "I'll do everything I can to help."

"I think he'll need it," said Dr. Carson. "I'm also worried about a fight he had today with Jake Blocker."

"Chip had a fight with Jake Blocker?" Becky asked.

"Apparently," replied her father. "And if he were ever to injure somebody, not only would my experiment be a failure, but I'd be responsible for hurting another human being." Dr. Carson began mixing up a batch of multiflex plastic to patch Chip's burned skin.

"He won't hurt anybody," replied Becky, looking at the data on the screen about the fight. "Your program won't let him, you've told me yourself."

"That's true," said the scientist. "Even so, I'm going to go over the program and make sure that there aren't any problems with it."

"Okay, Pops. Listen, I left some dinner in the oven for you. Don't stay up too late." She kissed her father good night and ran upstairs to get ready for bed.

After Dr. Carson repaired the android's skin, he went over several of the questions and problems that Chip had encountered. He added more verbal responses and included several new logical concepts to the android's conflict-resolution program. It was nearly 3 A.M. when he finished, but he felt sure that his creation was ready for anything that he might encounter.

Chip's next day at school went much more smoothly than the others had gone. After his last class, he waited for Becky by her locker so that they could walk home together. While he was waiting, Tad Taggart ran up to him. "Thanks for helping me escape from Jake yesterday," he said gratefully. "I hope he didn't hurt you."

"No, he just pushed me around a little," answered Chip.

Nervously, Tad said, "Chip, I have a confession to make. Can you keep a secret?"

"Where do you want me to keep it?"

Before Tad could answer, Becky came around the corner. "Hi!" she said to Chip. "Who's your friend?"

Chip introduced Tad. "He wants me to keep a secret," he added.

"You can't have any secrets from me," Becky told Chip with a grin. She turned to Tad. "My brother and I share everything."

"Well," said Tad. "I guess it's okay if I tell you. But don't tell anyone else."

"Okay," Becky replied.

But just at that moment, Erin Jeffries joined the kids. "Hi, you guys. Hi, Chip. Are you getting ready to go home? Maybe we could walk together."

"No!" Becky said abruptly. "What I mean is, Chip isn't getting ready to go home. We're going to meet our father and run some errands for him."

"But . . ." Chip began to disagree.

Becky quickly cut him off. "I forgot to tell you, Chip. We've got to meet Dad right away."

"That's too bad," Erin said to the android. "I was hoping to talk some more. Well, maybe I'll go to gymnastics practice after all. My backflips could use work." She turned to leave and gave Chip a big smile. "See you later," she said, gazing into his eyes.

"Goodbye," Chip replied.

"Good riddance," Becky said under her breath.

"Let's go meet Dad," said Chip.

"I guess I better go too," said Tad, edging away.

Becky grabbed his arm and yanked him back. "No way, you're staying right here."

"*I* don't want to see your dad," Tad replied, squirming in Becky's tight grip. "I see enough of him in school."

"We're not really seeing Dad," answered Becky. "I only said that to get rid of Erin. I don't want anyone else to know what we're doing." She pulled Tad closer and said, "Now tell us this secret of yours."

Tad leaned closer to Becky and Chip and whispered conspiratorially, "Mr. Gutman asked me to look after Chip because he thinks that he's the one who broke into the school, set fire to the cafeteria, and stole the sports trophies."

"Oh, no!" wailed Becky. "Chip's innocent. You've got to convince him my brother couldn't possibly be a thief and a firebug."

"I'm not any kind of bug," said Chip. "I didn't steal the trophies either."

"I believe you," answered Tad. "But convincing Mr. Gutman won't be so easy."

"You've got to do it!" said Becky. "If only we could find out who did those awful things. What kind of creep would set fire to their own school?"

"Jake Blocker's the biggest creep I know,"

83

said Tad. "Did you get away from him okay yesterday, Chip?"

"Yes," replied the android. He activated his logic program and analyzed the situation. *If a creep is a bad person, then Jake Blocker is a bad person. If he's bad, he might do bad things. Stealing is bad. Jake might be the thief, though others could be bad too.*

"Do you think Jake's the thief?" asked Becky.

"I don't know. I guess he could be," replied Tad. "He almost got kicked out of school for fighting."

"But, really, it could be anyone," cautioned Becky. "We can't accuse somebody without proof." She thought for a moment and then snapped her fingers. "I've got it! Instead of keeping an eye on my brother, why don't you watch Jake Blocker? Then we can find out if he's the thief or not."

Tad shook his head. "No way," he said. "I'd have to be crazy to do that."

"But you've got to help my brother," pleaded Becky. "The whole school thinks he's a criminal."

Tad started to back away, but Becky grabbed him by the arm. "I think you owe it to Chip," she said. "It's pretty crummy, your agreeing to spy on him like that. And look how he helped you yesterday."

"I'm not a spy!" protested Tad. "Mr. Gutman just asked me to make friends with Chip because he's new here and doesn't know anyone."

"But you said he suspected Chip of stealing the trophies and setting fire to the school," snapped Becky.

"I know," answered Tad, "but old Gutbelly suspects everybody, especially someone new in town."

"Maybe so," replied Becky. "But he seems determined to pin everything on my brother. You've got to help us find out who really committed those crimes."

"Okay, okay," agreed Tad reluctantly.

"Great!" cried Becky, slapping him on the back. "You and Chip should secretly follow Jake and watch every move he makes. If he's the vandal, I bet he'll do something to give himself away."

"I guess we could do that," answered Tad.

"What should I do?" asked the android.

"Go with Tad," said Becky. "Follow Jake this afternoon and see what he does, but don't let yourself be seen, okay?"

"I'll do it," replied Chip.

Becky bent over and whispered in her brother's ear, "Don't tell Dad about this. He might not like it, but if you can prove that you're innocent, he'll be really pleased."

The android was programmed to please his father, so he agreed.

"I'd go with you today," explained Becky, "but I've got a piano lesson. Be careful!" She waved goodbye and rushed down the hall.

"How can we find Jake Blocker?" asked Tad. "He could be anywhere."

Chip examined his memory banks and studied the information on Jake Blocker, using his dynakinetic logic circuits. Then he said, "He is probably waiting two blocks north of here, because that's where he was yesterday. If we go one block east, two blocks north, and half a block west, we could see him, but he wouldn't be able to see us."

"It's worth a try," said Tad. "It's the only lead we've got, so let's go."

Following Chip's route, the two boys were soon walking down Green Street. The android activated his visual pattern-recognition program and scanned for any signs of the bully. There was nothing unusual in sight. His internal data directory of Carson's laws told him that Blocker ought to be nearby, so Chip turned on his heat-seeking infrascanner.

All of a sudden he detected a large, boy-shaped image behind a brown wooden fence. "He's over there," said the android, pointing.

"I don't see anything," Tad said nervously. "Let's go home and forget about it."

Chip's object-detection program saw that the image behind the fence was moving toward them. "We must hide," said Chip. He and Tad ducked behind a big red car.

"There he is," whispered Tad, peering around the car's fender.

Jake Blocker stepped out from behind the fence. He walked briskly down the street, right past Tad and Chip.

The android silently left his hiding place and tracked Jake with his long range autofocus visual detector, following at a safe distance.

"Wait for me," said Tad, trying to keep up with the android.

Chip and Tad followed Jake until they came to one of Harbor City's main streets. There Chip turned left.

"Are you sure he went this way?" asked Tad, breathing hard.

"Yes," said Chip. His tracking program was able to detect the bully two blocks away. Suddenly Chip stopped and pulled Tad into an open fruit market.

"Hey!" yelled Tad. "We're supposed to follow Jake Blocker, not buy groceries!"

Chip's object-detection program reported that Jake had turned around and was coming back this way! "We must hide," said the android.

No customers were inside and the aproned

clerk was busy washing lettuce in the back. Chip stepped behind a tall shelf. "Jake Blocker will be walking by here in eleven seconds," he said.

Tad slipped behind the door. He peeked outside. "You must be psychic. Here he comes!" he exclaimed. He darted behind the shelf and huddled next to Chip. The boys waited silently. Tad's heart was pounding. Sure enough, Jake walked into the fruit market and began piling things in a basket.

Since Chip was well hidden, he examined his surroundings. He noticed a huge pile of round balls stacked up on a nearby counter.

The android checked his memory banks, but he couldn't figure out what the objects were. He had digital pictures of apples and tennis balls, but he didn't have any information about these orange-colored spheres. Reaching over, he pulled one out from the bottom of the pile.

Bump-bumpety-bump! The oranges spilled out of their neatly piled stack and rolled all over the floor. Jake heard the commotion, turned around, and spotted Chip and Tad.

"Run for it!" yelled Tad, zooming out the door.

"Run for what?" asked Chip, as Tad disappeared out of sight.

The clerk rushed over to Chip and began yelling at him. "It took me *hours* to stack those oranges!" he yelled. "I should make you pay damages."

88

"Why don't you make him put all the oranges back?" said Jake with a mischievous grin.

"Hi, my name is Chip," said the android, not sure what to do. Jake might leave at any moment, and he had to be ready to follow him, as Becky had told him to do.

"I don't care what your name is," snapped the clerk. "Now pick them up before I call the cops."

Chip began picking up the oranges. He put one layer on the table, but when he tried to stack up a second layer, the oranges tumbled onto the floor again. This was not a task he'd been programmed for.

For a few minutes, Jake watched Chip with amusement, and then continued his shopping. The next time he looked at his watch he realized he'd been in the market for over an hour. "I'd better get home with these groceries or Mom'll ground me again," he grumbled.

As he passed by Chip, the android fumbled again and sent the oranges rolling onto the floor. "It looks like you'll be here all night," snickered Jake as he headed out the door.

Customers came and went as the helpless android spent another hour working away. At last the oranges were neatly stacked. "Can I go home now?" Chip asked the clerk when he was finally done. It was 6:15.

"Yes, but don't come back in here again! Now get out before you wreck something else."

89

Chip rushed out of the store. "Wait a minute," shouted the clerk. "Come back here!"

"You told me never to come back again," answered the android.

"I just wanted to apologize," said the clerk in a friendlier voice. "I know you didn't mean to knock over the oranges, and you were a good sport to pick them all up. Take one for yourself."

Chip walked back inside and reached toward the bottom of the pile! The clerk leaped forward and stopped him just in time. "No, like this, like this!" he said, picking an orange from the top of the stack and handing it to the mechanical boy.

Chip looked at it for several seconds. "Is this something to eat?" he asked at last.

"No, you stick it in your ear!" yelled the clerk. "Now get out!"

The clerk watched with amazement as Chip walked out of the store, trying to put the orange in his ear. "That kid is a lunatic," he muttered, taking off his apron. "Or else he has the weirdest sense of humor I've ever seen."

CHAPTER 8

Chip turned the corner and raced up the walk to the Carsons' house. He opened the door and ran inside, intending to go to his room and recharge his dangerously low batteries.

The living room was full of people! Chip's pattern-recognition program recognized his father and sister, Mr. Duckworth, and Mr. Gutman. He had not met the men in blue uniforms, but his logic circuits told him that they were police officers.

"Chip!" cried Dr. Carson when the android appeared. "I was worried sick about you. Are you okay?"

"Yes, Dad. Can I go to my room?"

"Wait a minute," said Dr. Carson. "Tell these people where you were after school."

Chip activated his electrologic index of conflict resolution before answering. Becky had told him not to tell about following Jake, but she'd said nothing about telling *where* he'd gone. The android said, "I was at the fruit market on Hamilton Street."

"All this time?" asked Mr. Gutman.

"I was there from four-o-one to six-fifteen," Chip answered.

A friendly looking police officer, with a name tag marked Simpson, laughed. "You'll have to do better than that. Where were you around four-thirty?"

"At the fruit market," said Chip. "The minute is up, can I go to my room now?"

"Can't he go?" pleaded Becky. "He wouldn't steal anything! He just got lost."

"Is that true, Chip?" asked Dr. Carson.

"No," replied the android. "I knew where I was all afternoon."

"Chip, were you at the school?" his father asked.

"Yes," answered Chip.

"Aha!" shouted Mr. Duckworth, clutching his whistle. "I knew it!"

"Wait a minute," said Dr. Carson. *"When* were you at the school?"

Chip didn't answer. He stood there and waited.

"Answer the question, son," said Officer Simpson.

"I was waiting a minute," said Chip.

"None of your smart remarks!" said the principal. "You're in serious trouble."

"From seven-fifty-one A.M. to three-thirty-four P.M.," replied the android.

Dr. Carson put his arm around Chip. "I'm sure my boy is innocent," he said firmly. "You have no proof to suggest otherwise. He says he was at the fruit market and I believe him."

"Mind if I use your phone?" asked Officer Simpson.

"Go ahead," replied Dr. Carson.

Simpson called the fruit market, but there was no answer, so he told Marin, the other officer, "We'll check it out tomorrow."

"I want this boy arrested tonight," exclaimed Mr. Duckworth. "I'm sure he's the one responsible for stealing the computer."

"Computer?" repeated Chip.

"Yes," said his father. "There was another robbery at school this afternoon. The portable computer was taken."

"Playing innocent, huh?" scoffed Mr. Duckworth.

Officer Simpson shook his head. "We have no evidence that Chip is involved with this. Whoever took the computer left no fingerprints."

"Search the house," ordered Mr. Duckworth.

"You can't search the house without a warrant," said Becky.

"It's all right," said Dr. Carson. "We have nothing to hide. You're welcome to search if it will convince you that my son hasn't done anything illegal."

"Thanks," said Officer Marin. "We won't take long."

The officers searched the upstairs first, then Chip's room and the rest of the first floor. They were in the basement for only a moment when Simpson called upstairs, "Dr. Carson, will you come down here, please?"

Dr. Carson went downstairs and everyone else followed him. Officer Simpson pointed to a computer on the workbench. "Is this the stolen computer?" he asked.

"No, that's mine," answered Dr. Carson. "I have the sales slip somewhere around here."

Mr. Gutman examined the computer carefully. "It's similar, but it's not the same model. It isn't ours," he said regretfully.

Mr. Duckworth glanced around the cluttered basement. "Anything could be hidden down here, officers," he said. "I'm sure this boy is the thief. Arrest him!"

"Don't tell us how to do our job," said Officer Marin. "I know what a computer looks like, and while this place looks like a NASA tracking station, there's nothing down here that fits the description of the school computer. Come on, Joe," he added. "Let's check out some other leads."

"Sorry to have troubled you, Dr. Carson," said Officer Simpson as they trooped upstairs.

"I understand," replied Chip's father. "I hope you find the person responsible soon, so my son's reputation will be cleared up."

At the front door, Mr. Gutman told Mr. Duckworth to wait outside for him. Then he turned to Dr. Carson and said, "Listen, I'm very sorry about all this. Duckworth had convinced me that your boy had something to do with this mess, but I'll treat him as innocent until proven guilty."

"Thanks," said Dr. Carson. "I know Duckworth just wants his trophies back. And Chip's a good boy, but he's not used to this new town and new school."

"I understand," replied the principal. He shook hands with Dr. Carson and left.

Dr. Carson shut the front door and faced the android. "Now, Chip, where were you? You couldn't have been at a fruit market for two hours!"

"I was there for two hours, thirteen minutes, and forty-two seconds," replied the android truthfully.

"What were you doing?" asked Dr. Carson irritably. "Did your batteries run down?"

"Don't pick on him!" said Becky, rushing over and hugging her brother. "He has enough trouble."

"Sorry," sighed Dr. Carson. "I'm just on edge because all those people were here. I was really afraid they'd find out Chip's secret."

"What *were* you doing in the market, Chip?" asked Becky.

"I was stacking these things," said the android, pulling an orange out of his pocket. "The man there said you're supposed to put them in your ear."

Becky took the orange and began peeling it. "These are for eating, silly. They wouldn't fit in anyone's ear, except maybe an elephant's."

"At least you didn't steal the school's computer," said Dr. Carson. "When someone broke into the school this afternoon and stole the computer, Mr. Duckworth immediately decided you did it. When you weren't here and they accused you, it really had me worried. Why didn't you call me on your radio if you had to stay and stack oranges?"

"That's my fault, Pops," answered Becky. "I told him not to tell you what he was doing."

"Why not, young lady?"

"Because Chip was going to find out who'd stolen the trophies and set fire to the cafeteria," she replied. "I'm sorry."

Her father sighed. "I guess I understand," he said. "But please don't ever tell Chip *not* to tell me anything! His logic can't distinguish when it's important not to follow your orders."

"I promise I won't," said Becky. She bit into an orange section. "I guess my own logic isn't always so good either. I just wanted to help Chip, that's all." She offered part of the orange to her father as a peace offering and he smiled as he accepted it.

"Chip needs all the help he can get," Dr. Carson pointed out. "My experiment will be ruined if everyone thinks my creation is a criminal!"

"I'll do everything I can to help," promised Becky. "Maybe I can find out who the real criminal is!"

"Actually, I'd rather you just kept an eye on Chip," said her father.

"Is she going to put one of her eyes on me?" said the android. "Wouldn't that hurt her?"

"Yuk! Don't be disgusting," said Becky. "Both of my eyes are staying in my head!"

"Very nice eyes they are, too," said her father. "Now go finish your homework while I make sure Chip's all right."

"I'm only—" began the android.

"Yeah, we know," giggled Becky. "You're only half right!"

"Upstairs!" shouted her father.

Becky plodded up to her room while Dr. Carson took Chip down to the basement and stored the day's events in the main computer.

Then, weary beyond exhaustion, he led the android up to his room on the first floor, where Chip changed into a clean red-striped shirt and tan slacks. Dr. Carson then plugged him into his battery charger and went up to his own room to sleep.

The next day was a rough one for the mechanical boy. Word had gotten out that the school computer had been stolen, and someone had started the rumor that Chip was the thief.

At lunchtime, the android walked into the cafeteria and sat down next to Jenny Driscoll and her friends. "We know you didn't do it," said Jenny with a reassuring smile.

"Yeah," said Erin, looking concerned. "I'll never believe you could do anything like that. I'll even tell Mr. Gutman myself."

"Me, too!" said Cristy from the end of the table.

Under his breath, Mario muttered to Scott, "Oh no, now there are two of them after Chip."

Alex slapped the android on the back and said, "We're behind you all the way."

Chip swiveled his head around and checked in back of him. "You're sitting next to me," he said. "How can you be behind me?"

"*I'm* behind you now, creep," said a familiar voice. Jake Blocker towered over the android. "I hear you stole the school computer!"

"I don't hear that," said Chip, turning up his audio program.

"Beat it, Blockhead," said Jenny. "Chip's too nice to go around stealing. That's the kind of thing you'd do."

"Yeah? Who says?" replied the bully, making a fist so tight that his arm muscles bulged underneath his shirt.

"Jenny said it," responded Chip. "Is something wrong with your hearing?"

"Chip!" cried Jenny. "Whose side are you on?"

The android tipped back his chair and looked to his left and right. "Mario is on one side of me and you're on the other. I'm—"

"Quit clowning!" growled Jake. "I don't like people who steal things. Then everybody blames me!"

"Since I didn't steal anything, you must like me," said the android.

Jake laughed. "That's right, you and me are pals, real pals," he said sarcastically, leaning on the back of the android's chair. All of a sudden it flipped over backward.

Crash! Chip sprawled across the floor, and everybody jumped up to help him, including Jake Blocker. "Hey, I didn't mean to knock you down," he said.

"You'd better get out of here before one of the teachers comes over and wants to kick you out of school again," warned Jenny. She stepped in Jake's path.

"It was an accident," explained Jake. "Here, I'll help him up." The boy reached down and put an arm under Chip's shoulder. Even though the android's steel body was very heavy, enough other kids helped that no one noticed the mechanical boy's weight.

The bell rang. "Come on, let's get out of here before Jake 'helps' you again," said Alex.

"It was a mistake, I tell you," pleaded Jake. "When I knock somebody over, I'll admit it. I'm no coward!"

Everybody was rushing to the next class. Scott and P.J. steered Chip through the crowd to the cafeteria door, leaving Jake behind. When they got out into the hall, P.J. said, "I've been talking to your sister, Chip. Maybe she's right about Jake's being the thief. He might be trying to put the blame on you."

"Becky's only half right," answered the android.

"Which half?" said P.J.

"Oh, oh," interrupted Mario. "Here he comes again."

Jake walked up with Chip's red book bag in his hand. "Here, creep," he said, throwing it to Chip. "You left this behind."

The android's object-detection program enabled him to catch the bag easily while his verbal-response program analyzed Blocker's last statement. "That's my book bag, not my behind," he replied.

"Why don't I kick it and find out?" snarled Jake.

"Let's get out of here," said P.J., pulling Chip away.

The second bell rang and Jake headed down the hall. "I'll see you after school, thief!" he yelled as he disappeared into the crowd.

"Don't worry," said Jenny. "We'll stick with you all the way."

"With glue?" asked Chip.

Jenny laughed and replied, "In your case, I think we could use Krazy Glue! Come on, everybody, we're all going to be late."

CHAPTER 9

When the bell rang at the end of Chip's English class, he gathered up his books and headed for the door. "Hey, wait for me," said Erin as she scrambled after him. "You know, Chip," she said, "if you want me to, I'll go talk to Mr. Gutman and tell him that you couldn't have had anything to do with any of those robberies."

"I can tell him myself," replied Chip. "Do you have any evidence about the robberies?"

"No, but I want to help you. I know how tough old Gutman can be. Last year he almost suspended two guys for tracking mud into the hall! You should really be careful of him *and* Mr. Duckworth. That Duckbrain is even tougher. I've heard stories about how he goes to absent students' homes to find out if they're

really sick. I'll tell you who's really sick—
Duckworth!"

"Did someone go to his home to find out?"
Chip interrupted.

"No," Erin laughed. "*Everybody* knows he's
sick. I hate the way the two of them are blaming
you for something I know you didn't do. I
believe you. You couldn't possibly be hiding
anything. Won't you please let me speak to Mr.
Gutman for you?"

"That's impossible," replied the android.
"Only I can speak for myself."

"Well, if that's what you want," answered
Erin. "But if you change your mind, just let me
know. Mr. Gutman lives down the street from
me and he's been a friend of the family for
years." She turned right and Chip stopped.

"I have to go this way," he said, pointing to
the left.

"Okay," replied Erin. "See you later." She
stood silently, watching Chip as he hurried
down the hall.

He went straight to the computer lab. The
wooden table where the portable computer sat
yesterday was empty. Several kids were at their
black-and-white terminals, but the android's
audio tracking program told him that the lab
was much quieter than it had been yesterday.

"Too bad the computer's gone," said Tad,
when Chip entered the lab. "I was going to

103

show you a video game I wrote, but it can only be run on the portable."

"You want to play a game?" said the android. "Guess a number between one and ten."

"That sounds real boring," replied Tad. "Did Jake Blocker beat you up yesterday?"

"No," answered Chip. "But he pushed me down today at lunch. He said that I stole the computer."

"Yeah," replied Tad. "The whole school's talking about it. This afternoon Mr. Gutman wants me to report on your activities. Too bad I can't tell him what you were doing at four-thirty yesterday. That's when the computer was stolen."

"I was picking up oranges at the fruit stand," said Chip. "It took two hours, thirteen minutes, and forty-two seconds."

"Since I was only there for a few minutes," Tad said, "I can't tell him that's true. I hope you don't get into too much hot water over this."

"Does Mr. Gutman want to give me a bath?" asked Chip. "I'm not dirty."

"Why should he give you a bath?" Tad asked with a frown.

"Why else would he put me in hot water?"

"Oh, I get it," grinned Tad. "I'm glad you can joke at a time like this."

"It's one-fifteen," said the mechanical boy, checking his internal time clock.

"Time to get to work," replied Tad. "While

I'm debugging my new video game program, how about if you go to the library and get me the books on this list."

Chip took the list. "You said your game was written for the stolen computer," he said. "Without a computer, how can you debug a video game?"

Pointing to his head, Tad bragged, "The computer may be gone and I may not have my own portable computer, but I do have one up here."

The android pointed to his chest. "Mine is here," he replied.

"Yeah, sure, whatever. Now get those books and be back here before the bell rings, okay?"

Chip grabbed his red book bag and headed for the door. "Hey," Tad called, "you can leave your bag here. I don't want you to get your books mixed up with mine. And don't steal anything on the way!"

"Okay," said the android. He left his bag on a table, went to the library, handed the list to the librarian, and checked out the books.

Just as he reached the door on his way out, Erin threw it open and said, "Hi, Chip!"

The android missed the door handle, causing him to drop a book. Erin bent over, picked it up, and continued talking. "The other day you said maybe we could go to the Burger Bear and talk. I've been looking forward to spending some more time with you. Maybe I can still convince you to let me talk to Mr. Gutman. I'm so sorry they're giving you such a hard time. You really don't deserve it. It makes me angry just thinking about them. I'd like to do a few cartwheels across their chests!"

"I can't spend time with you today," answered Chip. "My father says I have to go straight home after school."

"Oh, you could stop off at the Burger Bear for just a minute, couldn't you?" Erin asked, reaching over and touching Chip gently on the arm.

"There's so much I'd like to know about you."

"What would you like to know?"

"Most of all I want to know what you were like as a little boy." She inched closer to the android, taking his high-resolution, multiflex plastic hand in hers. "Maybe you could show me some pictures. I just love little kids. I'd like to be a kindergarten teacher when I grow up." She paused, looking deeply into his blue nylon eyes. "Won't you please come to the Burger Bear with me?"

"No," Chip answered firmly. "I must do as my father says."

"What are you, some kind of robot?" Erin teased.

Chip's mouth dropped open and his electrologic index of conflict resolution tried to decide how to answer her. He was programmed

106

never to reveal his android identity, but he was also instructed to answer all questions.

Before he could resolve the conflict, Erin said, "Gee, Chip, don't look so shocked. I was only joking."

"Oh," he replied. "I have to get back to the computer lab now. See you later."

"Great!" said Erin, as the android left the library.

When Chip returned to the lab, Tad was busy making notes on the printout of his video game. The android peered over his shoulder and analyzed the game. "It'll crash in line six-twenty," said Chip.

"How can you tell that?" asked Tad in surprise. "I was up until midnight last night trying to run this game, and I couldn't get it to work."

"It'll crash. You've got a GOTO where you should have a GOSUB," explained Chip. "Your program will try to return to the wrong place."

Tad looked at his program for several moments, then said, "I see what you mean. Boy, if I'm not careful, they'll make you the computer lab monitor. You're really a hot programmer."

"I'm not any warmer than room temperature," said the android, checking his internal thermostat.

The bell rang. Chip said goodbye and went to Mrs. Quackenbush's biology class.

107

"Hey," said Stephanie cheerfully, when the android sat down at her table. "What's new?"

"New is something that is not old," replied the android.

"What's old?" said Sid.

"Something that is not new," said Chip.

Mrs. Quackenbush began handing out sheets of paper. "Oh, oh," said Sid. "These look like pictures of the insides of frogs!"

"What were you expecting," laughed Stephanie, "the insides of an elephant?"

"I think I'm going to get sick. Maybe I could go to the nurse," said Sid. "This is so *disgusting.*"

"Quiet, please, class," said Mrs. Quackenbush. "I want you to study these pictures carefully. On Monday we'll begin analyzing the anatomy of amphibians."

"Is that frogs?" asked Sid.

"Yes. Frogs are amphibians," said Mrs. Quackenbush. "The word comes from the Greek word *amphibios* and means a double life. Frogs live both in the water and on the land."

"Sort of like my grandparents, who go to Florida every winter," said Stephanie.

Sid snickered.

"Are your grandparents frogs?" inquired Chip.

"Do *I* look like a frog?" asked Stephanie indignantly.

The lesson was interrupted when a student

108

came into the room and handed a note to Mrs. Quackenbush. The teacher read it, then said, "Chip, you're wanted in the principal's office."

The android stood up. Stephanie clutched his hand and said, "Goodbye, kid. We'll visit you in prison!"

"Prison might not be so bad," commented Sid. "He won't have to cut up any frogs there."

"Be brave," said Stephanie, more seriously. "We know you're not the thief, Chip."

"Thanks," the android replied, walking out the door.

When Chip arrived at the principal's office, the gray-haired secretary said, "Mr. Gutman will see you now."

"How can he see me?" asked Chip. "The door is closed."

"You kids!" the secretary laughed. "Open the door and he'll see you plenty."

The android opened the door and found himself facing Mr. Gutman and Mr. Duckworth. "Come in, Chip," said the principal.

When the door was closed, Mr. Gutman said, "I'm sorry to do this, Chip, but we have reason to suspect that you have stolen property in your book bag. Let me see it."

Chip held it up.

"No, open it and dump out everything on my desk," Mr. Gutman instructed tiredly.

The android did as he was told. Out came books, a notebook, pencils, and a calculator.

109

"Aha!" said Mr. Duckworth triumphantly. He picked up a blue spiral-bound book. "This is the reference manual to the stolen computer. Where did you get this?"

Chip looked at the book. He had never seen it before. "I got it out of the bag," the android answered.

"How did it get *in* there, young man?" demanded Mr. Gutman.

"I don't know," Chip said.

"We've got you red-handed," said the gym teacher. "You might as well tell the truth."

Chip examined his hands. They were still flesh colored. "What do you want to know?" he asked.

"For starters," said the principal, "where did you hide the computer?"

"I didn't hide it," said Chip.

"Then what did you do with it?" yelled Mr. Duckworth.

"I didn't do anything with it." At that moment the last bell rang, and Chip asked, "Can I go home now?"

"Not yet," replied Mr. Gutman. "I'm afraid we have to call the police first." He dialed the phone and had a short conversation with Officer Simpson. "They'll be here in fifteen minutes," he said, as he hung up the phone.

Chip's electrologic index of conflict resolution told him that this was an emergency situation. If the police took him to the station, they might find out he was an android. He activated his internal interface radio and gave his father another silent call for help.

"This is Becky," came the reply. "Dad's at an after-school meeting and I'm waiting in his classroom. I didn't see you when school let out. Where are you?"

Chip explained the situation without anyone else hearing. "Don't go anywhere," Becky told him. "I'll see what I can do to help."

"Okay," replied Chip. He switched off the radio.

"Didn't you hear what I said?" asked Mr. Duckworth crossly.

The android had turned off his external audio sensors while he called for help. "No, what did you say?"

"I said you'll sit in the next room and wait for the police. Now march!"

Chip raised his legs up high as he stomped into the next room. Mr. Duckworth locked the green metal door and muttered, "I've got you now!"

The android waited. After a few minutes, he heard a tapping on the window. He turned and saw the top of Becky's head. Cautiously she inched up until her brown eyes peeked over the sill. When she saw that no teachers were in sight, she whispered, "Open the window!"

Chip went over and pulled on the window. It was locked on both sides, but the power of his synchronized sector motors easily broke the locks, and the window flew open.

"Climb out quick!" said Becky in a whisper.

"They told me to wait here for the police," answered the android.

"Come on!" said the girl urgently. "If the police get you, Dad's experiment will be ruined. Hurry before it's too late!"

"It's three-fifteen and ten seconds," reported Chip.

"Quit acting like the telephone time recording and *come out here,*" hissed Becky.

Chip scrambled out the window. "What do we do now?" he asked.

"We're going to find out who the real thief is!" said Becky. "It's the only way to keep you out of the scrap heap." She grabbed her brother's hand and quickly led him away from the building.

At that moment, Mr. Duckworth's head popped out the window. "Come back here or I'll clobber you!"

"He's just like Jake Blocker," said the android.

"Well, don't worry about it. That's exactly who we're going to find," said Becky, running down the sidewalk.

"Mr. Duckworth's, climbing out of the window," said Chip. "Shouldn't we go back? He said we'd get clobbered if we didn't."

"No! We've got to find Jake Blocker! Keep

112

running! Don't look back!" yelled Becky, as she raced toward a big white bus.

The gym teacher chased them down the block, but Becky leaped onto the bus and yanked her brother in after her, just before the folding doors slammed shut.

Mr. Duckworth pounded on the glass, but the bus driver, a young woman, yelled, "Take the next bus!"

"Stop! I'm a teacher!" he shouted.

"I don't care if you're the king of France!" The driver gunned the engine and the bus shot forward.

"I didn't know Mr. Duckworth was the king of France," said Chip.

"He's not," replied Becky, sitting down. "He's not even the prime minister. Now be quiet while I think."

Chip sat quietly and waited. Mr. Duckworth angrily shook his fist at the bus, as it rapidly moved down the street.

CHAPTER 10

"How can we find Jake Blocker?" Becky asked.

"Yesterday he was hiding behind a fence on Green Street," replied Chip. "Tad and I followed him from there to the fruit market."

"Then Green Street's our next stop," said Becky. She pulled the cord to signal that they wanted to get out. "I sure hope we can prove that Jake is the criminal. Otherwise we'll be in hot water."

"I'm not programmed for swimming," said the android, "no matter what temperature the water is."

The bus jolted to a stop and Becky jumped out. Chip followed behind. "I don't see Jake," she said as the bus pulled away.

Activating his infrared vision, the android

scanned the neighborhood. "He's not behind the fence," he reported.

"Then we'll just have to look for him and hope the police don't find us first," replied Becky. "Keep your eyes peeled for any sign of that Blockhead."

"If I peel my eyes, I won't be able to see," said the mechanical boy.

"I meant, look for him," explained Becky.

"I will," answered the android. He and Becky walked cautiously up the street. Using his pattern-recognition program at full power, Chip scanned the area ahead. *Over there.* "I see Jake now. He's coming toward us," Chip reported.

"I don't see anything," said Becky.

"He's two blocks away."

"Sometimes I'm amazed at your powers," said Becky. "All right. We'll hide until he goes by and then we'll follow him. He's *got* to be the crook!"

Becky and Chip crouched behind a parked car as Jake strutted past them. When he was a safe distance ahead, Becky and Chip followed him down Green Street. Instead of hiding behind the fence as he had done the day before, he headed for a group of shops on Willow Avenue and went into a computer store.

"What's an idiot like him doing in a computer store?" said Becky, as she ducked down behind an old black truck.

"Why don't you ask him?" asked Chip.

115

"A good detective doesn't ask, she finds out!" exclaimed Becky. "We'll just wait until he leaves and then we'll ask the store clerk."

"How can you ask the clerk after he leaves?" wondered her brother.

"No, no, no! We'll ask the clerk after *Jake* leaves," said Becky shaking her head. "I'll sure be glad when Pops improves your programming!"

"Here he comes now," said Chip.

"Who? Dad?" Becky asked. Then she laughed and said, "Now you've got me doing it!" She spotted Jake and whispered, "Hush!"

Jake walked out of the store with a blue paper bag under his arm. "Shouldn't we follow him now?" inquired Chip. "If we go into the computer store, we might not be able to find Jake again."

"At least your logic circuits are working properly," said Becky. "I'll follow Jake and you go into the store and find out what he bought."

"How will I find you?"

"I've got Dad's radio," she pointed out. "I'll call you and tell you where to meet me."

Becky slipped away to follow Jake, and Chip entered the computer store. A short blond clerk came up and asked, "May I help you?"

"Yes," said Chip. "What did Jake Blocker buy?"

"Who's Jake Blocker?"

"He's the one who's always trying to beat me up."

The young clerk smiled. "This isn't a police station. Would you like to try out one of our video games?" he asked.

"Sure," said the android. "But what did Jake Blocker buy? My sister wants to know. She said it's very important."

"Is Jake Blocker the boy who was just in the store?"

"Yes," replied Chip.

"Okay. Just a moment. I think it was just floppy disks, but let me check. All of our sales information is on the computer, of course. Why don't you try out this new game, *Cosmic Bumpercars*. I'll check the records while you play."

The clerk led Chip over to a demonstration computer and loaded the game disk. The android scanned the instructions printed on the screen, picked up the black joystick and began playing. He swiftly guided the brightly colored video bumpercars across the screen.

A horde of hungry hermit crabs blocked the tiny car's path, but Chip blasted each attacker before its claws could clip off his headlights. Next, swirling clouds of purple pandas, ravenous bananas, and dancing donuts threatened his vehicle, but the reflex mechanisms built into the android's dynakinetic circuits were more than a match for the simple program.

117

Suddenly, in the middle of his game, Chip noticed a small mistake in the action of the game play. The android's electrologic index of conflict resolution told him that he should try to fix it.

Chip stopped playing and listed the program on the screen. After analyzing the program code, he made a few changes and ran the game again.

The clerk returned and said, "Pretty good game, huh?" Then his mouth dropped open as he noticed Chip's score. "Hey! How did you get such a high score? I wrote the game myself and *I've* never done that well!"

"I just followed the instructions," said the android. "Did you find out what Jake Blocker bought?"

"Yeah, but how did you destroy all the bananas?" said the bewildered clerk. "I made them go extra fast." He grabbed the joystick out of Chip's hand and began firing. "I don't understand it!" he muttered. "The game never played like this before."

"I shot the bananas by pressing the fire button. What did Jake Blocker buy?" Chip asked again.

"Oh, just some floppy disks," answered the clerk, intently playing the game. "Hey, will you show me how you destroyed the donuts?"

"Okay," replied Chip, "but as soon as my

118

sister calls, I've got to leave." The android took the joystick and began playing. The synchronized sector motors in his arm moved so fast that he was able to wipe all the donuts off the screen in seconds.

Then a wave of strange pink-and-green video creatures appeared. "What are *those?*" exclaimed the clerk. "I *created* this game, but I've never seen anything like them! I don't understand this at all."

Chip didn't answer, because he heard his sister's voice coming through his internal interface radio. "Chip, come quickly to the corner of Third and Main. Drop whatever you're doing and get here as fast as you can."

Chip obediently dropped the joystick on the floor, then raced out of the store. Pumping his leg motors as fast as he could, he ran down the street. Suddenly his pattern-recognition program detected a familiar shape ahead, a big muscular man with thick black hair. It was Mr. Duckworth!

"You won't get away from me this time!" he yelled as he ran toward the android.

Chip didn't stop to answer. He dodged away from the angry man and kept right on running. Mr. Duckworth made a grab for him as he went by, but the mechanical boy's sector motors were faster than any human legs.

As Mr. Duckworth watched the boy fade

119

from sight, he shook his head slowly and mumbled, "That boy isn't human!"

Chip flew down the street until he arrived at the corner of Third and Main. Becky was crouched down behind a tree. Jake Blocker was nowhere in sight.

"Here I am, Becky," said Chip.

"I don't need a pattern-recognition program to see that!" she laughed. "What did you find out at the computer store?"

"Their game of *Cosmic Bumpercars* had a mistake in it," he answered. "I fixed it for them."

"What about Jake?"

"He bought a box of floppy disks."

"That's proof enough for me," Becky decided. "I'm sure that a big dumb bully like Jake doesn't own a computer, so he must've stolen the school's computer and now he needs floppy disks to make it work."

"That's not logical," replied Chip. "You said he's dumb and that he wouldn't own a computer, so why would he steal one? Besides, Dad said plenty of dumb people own computers."

Becky sighed. "I guess you're right. The disks aren't proof enough. Just the same, I think it's suspicious that he's buying them. Anyway, Jake's the only suspect we've got."

"Where's Jake now?" asked Chip.

120

Becky pointed to a nearby bookstore. "He's in there. I'm going to phone the police and tell them that I suspect Jake. If that Blockhead comes out, you hold him."

"How can I do that?" asked the android. "My internal data directory of Carson's laws says I can't use force on another person."

"Don't argue! I'm a Carson too, and I'm telling you that if you let Jake escape, they'll arrest you!"

"Okay," said Chip. Becky's command didn't seem to contradict his father's laws, so the android waited while Becky ran to a phone booth a block away.

He didn't have long to wait. "Hey, creep, just the guy I want to pound," Jake said as he walked out of the bookstore.

"You have to stay here," replied Chip.

"Yeah, who says so?" growled Jake as he moved closer.

"My sister says so," answered the android.

"Your sister," sneered Jake. "Listen, I go where I want to, when I want to!" He reached out to push Chip aside, but the android dodged to the left.

"All right, all right, I'm too busy to fight you now, anyway," said Jake.

"You must stay here," insisted Chip.

"Why? Do you like me so much you can't stand to see me go?"

121

"No," replied the android. "You must wait until the police arrive."

"Police!" yelled Jake. "Are you crazy? I'm getting out of here!" He tried to run past the android, but Chip jumped in his path. Jake bounced off the mechanical boy's steel body and fell to the ground.

CHAPTER 11

"Carson, you're making me mad!" roared Jake, climbing to his feet. "I hate to do this, but you've got it coming." He reached back and swung at Chip, but the android quickly ducked down.

Jake backed off. "Now, look!" he cried.

"Look at what?" asked Chip.

"Never mind." Jake shook his head in disgust. "Why do you want the police to bother me? I haven't done anything wrong!"

"You bought floppy disks."

"So what? I paid for them. I've got the store receipt right here." He pointed to the blue paper bag under his arm.

"Becky thinks you're the one who stole the school computer. She's calling the police," said the android.

"You know I wasn't the one who took the computer," cried Jake. "I was in the fruit market with you when it was stolen."

Chip activated his dynakinetic logic circuits and replied, "Since you were in the fruit market with *me,* why did you accuse me of being the thief in the cafeteria today?"

"I was just making fun of you. If you were in real trouble, I'd tell them you were innocent."

"I'm in real trouble now," said the mechanical boy. "They found the manual for the stolen computer in my book bag after lunch today."

"Well, I didn't put it in there," said Jake. "I may push people around, but I'd never frame anybody."

Chip suddenly noticed Becky leave the phone booth and run away from him, down the street. He secretly called her on his internal interface radio. "I'm over here, Becky. Jake didn't steal the computer."

His sister's voice replied, "Find out why he bought the floppy disks if he didn't steal the computer. The phone was out of order and I'm going to find another one to call the police. You stay with Jake no matter what. That's an order!"

While Chip was still transmitting to Becky, Jake suddenly turned and ran. Because the android was temporarily distracted by his internal transmission, he didn't notice until Jake was halfway down the block. Instantly, he activated his legs' synchronized sector motors and ran after him as fast as he could. He caught up with Jake easily and ran in step beside him. "Why did you buy the floppy disks?" he asked. "Do you have a computer?"

"Me? A computer? You gotta be kidding," said Jake, still running. "Listen, why don't you quit bothering me?"

"Becky told me to find out why you bought the floppy disks," answered the android.

"Well, she doesn't have to know everything," answered Jake. "And—hey, look out!"

With lightning speed, Mr. Duckworth leaped around the corner and tackled the two boys. "Don't move or you'll get it," he yelled.

"We weren't doing anything," Jake said angrily.

"Maybe not, but that's for the police to find out," said the gym teacher grimly. "Now that I see the two of you together, it all makes sense!"

"You can't pin this computer stuff on me!" yelled Jake.

"How could he pin a computer on you?" asked Chip. "Computers are heavy. Wouldn't it fall off?"

Mr. Duckworth grabbed the blue bag out of Jake's hand. "Aha! Floppy disks," he said triumphantly. "Bought in your name, Jake Blocker. Maybe Carson here is just your unwitting accomplice!"

"He's unwitting all right, but not an accomplice. Neither one of us stole the computer!"

"Then why did you buy floppy disks?"

"I don't have to answer your questions!" Jake yelled. "I can buy anything I want."

Suddenly Chip heard his sister's voice on the internal interface radio. "Where are you, Chip?" she said.

"I'm at the corner of Beech and Oak. Mr. Duckworth and Jake are here with me," the android transmitted. "Mr. Duckworth thinks that Jake and I stole the computer and he wants to pin it on Jake, even though I told him it would fall off."

"Get away quickly, Chip!" ordered Becky frantically. "The police don't believe me. Run as fast as you can!"

The android switched into high speed and raced away, with Mr. Duckworth after him. Jake escaped in the other direction.

Once again, the speed of Mr. Duckworth's human muscles was not equal to the synchronized sector motors of a C-13 integrated electrologic android. Racing halfway around the block, Chip easily escaped and was soon out of the gym teacher's sight. He ran at full speed for two more blocks, then darted behind a yellow house to stop and give his batteries a rest.

Suddenly Jake Blocker sprinted around the corner. "Where'd you come from?" he said, jumping back in surprise. "Did you lose the Duckbrain?"

"I never had a duck's brain," answered the android.

Jake threw up his hands and shook his head in disbelief. "No, Duckworth! The big guy with the whistle around his neck!"

"I don't think he saw me run this way," answered Chip.

"Good," Jake said with a sigh of relief. "But now I'm out the price of a box of floppy disks!"

"Why did you buy them?" asked Chip. "Floppy disks aren't useful unless you have a computer."

"I promised I wouldn't tell," Jake said slowly. "But I'm beginning to wonder if I wasn't being framed myself."

"You aren't a picture," said Chip. "Why would somebody frame you?"

"That's what I've been asking myself," said Jake. "What do you know about that Taggart kid?"

"He's my friend," began the android, examining his electrologic memory banks. "He was supposed to help me get used to my new school. He programs computers."

Jake laughed. "He's not much of a friend. Twice he ran away when I was pushing you around."

"But he said he was my friend," replied Chip.

"Plenty of people would say that and then stab you in the back. Why don't we go pay him a little visit?"

"I don't know where he lives," said the android.

"I do," replied Jake. "He's the one who paid me to buy the floppy disks. Follow me."

As they walked down the street, Chip said, "But he doesn't have a computer either. He said so."

"I wouldn't know about that," replied Jake, "but he asked me to buy a computer book for him. It wasn't in the bookstore, though. I wonder if the little wimp was the one who stole the school's computer."

"We could ask him," said the android.

"Yeah, let's do that!"

Tad Taggart's house was only a few blocks away, and soon Chip and Jake were knocking on the door.

A short, brown-haired woman dressed in a business suit answered the door. "Hello, boys. Are you here to see Tad?" she asked.

"Yeah," said Jake. "Is he home?"

"I think so," replied the woman, opening the screen door. "I'm his mother. I just got home from work, but I'm pretty sure Tad's here." Mrs. Taggart called Tad and he ran downstairs.

"Hi, Jake," he said. "Come on up to my

room." Then he noticed Chip. "What are *you* doing here?" he asked.

"He's with me," said Jake.

"Then I guess Mr. Gutman didn't . . . uh, well, come on up," said Tad nervously.

The boys crossed the tidy but sparsely furnished living room and climbed the stairs to Tad's bedroom. Chip and Jake stepped over the clothes that were scattered across the floor and sat down on the unmade bed. Tad closed the door. "Well?" he said to Jake. "Where are the disks? Did you get the book?"

"I don't have them," answered Jake. "I couldn't find the book, and then we ran into Mr. Duckworth. He thought we were the ones who stole the computer, so he took the floppy disks away from me."

"That's too bad," said Tad, kicking the rug with the toe of his tennis shoe. "I know everybody thinks Chip took the computer, but why would the Duckbrain think you had anything to do with it?"

"Whenever something bad happens, people always think I did it," grumbled Jake. "I guess I just look mean or something."

Chip tried to solve a logic problem that his index of conflict resolution couldn't successfully compute. "Why did you ask Jake to buy floppy disks?" he asked Tad.

"I thought I told you not to tell anybody,"

Tad snapped at Jake. "Give me my money back."

"Get your disks from the Duckbrain," said Jake. "You can explain to him that they belong to *you*. I'm sure he doesn't think a teacher's pet would steal the school's computer."

"I didn't steal it!" Tad cried. "Why would I steal the computer when I can use it all I want anyway?"

Chip's logic circuits had processed something else that he didn't understand, and he needed to ask another question. "Today you told me that you ran your program last night, Tad," he said. "How could you do that if the computer had already been stolen?"

"Hey, good thinking, Chip," said Jake. "Answer that, Taggart!"

"I made a mistake," said Tad nervously.

"Yeah, I think you did," replied Jake triumphantly.

"No, I meant I ran my program yesterday," explained Tad. "Anyway, it's just Chip's word against mine."

"Then why did you want floppy disks?" persisted Chip.

"I like to have my own disks," Tad explained, "so none of the dumb kids at school will accidentally erase one of my programs. Mr. Gutman told me we'll have a new computer next week—the insurance will cover it. I just want to be ready when it arrives."

"I guess that makes sense," replied Jake. "But personally, I can think of lots of things I'd rather spend money on."

"You just don't understand how great computers are," said Tad. "Chip here likes computers, don't you?"

The android's verbal response program told him to say, "Computers are great."

"Not everybody has to play with them, though," replied Jake with a sneer. "You can have them if you want. I'm saving for a dirt-bike."

"I'll be able to buy a car when I win the big video game design contest," Tad said proudly. "My entry is almost finished."

"Big deal! There's lots of video games already," said Jake. He glanced around Tad's room. "This place sure is a mess."

"If you don't like it, you can leave."

"I'll do that," said Jake. "But there's one thing I don't quite understand. How did that computer manual get in Chip's book bag? I looked inside it at lunch and it wasn't in there then."

"How would I know?" said Tad, pacing across his room nervously. "Chip's my friend, so I won't accuse him of any crimes. He's got enough trouble already."

"With friends like you, I think I'd rather be by myself," said Jake. "Come on, Chip, let's go."

"Where are we going?"

"Anywhere else. This place not only looks like a pig sty, it smells like one."

"My room's a mess because I'm working on stuff too important to bother with little things like cleaning my room."

"Yeah, that's what I try to tell *my* Mom!" said Jake.

At that moment, Tad's mother walked into the room carrying a tray. "I thought you kids might like a snack," she said. She set a tray with potato chips and cans of root beer on Tad's desk.

"Great! Potato chips!" exclaimed Tad.

"I'm not covered with potatoes," said the android.

"I bet you get a lot of kidding about your name," said Jake. "People kid me about my name. Jake Blockhead they called me, until I learned how to beat people up."

"You boys have fun," said Mrs. Taggart. She left the room.

CHAPTER 12

Jake took a can of root beer and a big handful of potato chips. "Well, what do we have here?" he said. "I guess we can stay for a few more minutes." He gave the can a shake and threw it to Chip. When the android opened it, the root beer spewed all over the room. "Sorry about that," Jake said sarcastically.

"You did that on purpose," yelled Tad.

"Who *me?*"

"Yeah, you! Now my room's a mess!"

"It was already a mess," observed Chip.

"Good point," laughed Jake. "But I still wonder how that computer manual got in Chip's book bag."

"Obviously he put it there," said Tad, mop-

133

ping root beer off a computer printout. "Everybody knows he stole the computer!"

"That's true loyalty," said Jake.

"I can't help it. I know what he did," replied Tad.

Jake grabbed another handful of potato chips, dropping several on the carpet. "But *I* know Chip didn't steal the computer."

"How could you know that?" Tad asked. "The only way you could know that is if you were the thief."

"Sorry, Tad," replied Jake. "You're playing a dangerous game when you accuse me."

"Do you want to play a game?" asked the android. "Guess a number between one and ten."

"Later," said Jake impatiently. "I'm thinking."

"Don't strain yourself," said Tad.

"I won't stand for insults!"

"But you are standing," said Chip.

Suddenly, Jake began searching Tad's room. He opened and closed drawers, scattered papers everywhere, and pulled books off the shelf.

"Hey, cut that out!" yelled Tad.

But Jake didn't stop. He tore through everything in Tad's room.

At that moment, something strange started happening to Chip. The android's ionic thermostat was overheating and his cybernetic voltage

134

regulator detected dangerously high currents racing through his control wires!

It was the root beer.

Some of it had spilled on the android's body. Chip's high-resolution, multiflex plastic skin was impervious to water, but Dr. Carson had not thought to test it on root beer.

Only a drop had seeped through a small crack in the android's skin, but that was enough. It touched one of his electrologic chips, creating a short circuit.

Bzzzzt! The malfunctioning chip caused the android's internal interface radio to go wildly out of control. Instead of operating on the normal frequency, it started broadcasting on three different frequencies at once. The android was able to keep his expression normal, but inside, his electrologic circuits were going berserk! By switching over to spare circuits, he was able to stop the erratic voltages from burning out his sector motors, but none of Chip's error-detection circuits could tell him what was wrong. The radio continued to transmit silently without his knowing it.

Suddenly—*beep-beep-beep!*

"What's that noise?" asked Jake.

"I don't hear anything," said Tad. "Why don't you go away? I've got homework to do."

"It's Friday, dumbo!" sneered Jake. "Who does homework on Friday night?"

135

Beep-beep-beep!

"There's that noise again!" Jake walked around the room, listening carefully. He stopped at one of the walls and pressed his ear against it.

Meanwhile, Tad was becoming more and more nervous. "Go home!" he cried. "Or I'll call my mother."

"What will you call her?" asked Chip. So far his verbal response program was unaffected by the voltage surges which were sparking through his body, but other parts of him were not responding to the program. Still unaware that his internal radio was broadcasting signals, the android's external audio program picked up the strange noises.

Beep-beep-beep!

Chip turned on his audio tracking program and walked in the direction of the sound. "The beeps are coming from there," he said, pointing to the same wall.

Jake began feeling around the wall. "Nice wallpaper you got here," he said. "Hey, what's this rip in the paper?"

"GET OUT NOW!" yelled Tad.

As Chip got closer to the wall, the beeps grew louder. *BEEP-BEEP-BEEP!* The android activated his pattern-recognition program and analyzed the wall. His vision circuits detected the tear in the paper and saw a crack in the wall underneath. He reached out and pressed it.

Creeek! Part of the wall swung open.
BEEP-BEEP-BEEP-BEEP-BEEP!

"Hey! A secret panel!" Jake exclaimed, looking eagerly inside.

"Get away from there," screamed Tad, frantically grabbing at the opening in the wall.

"I found it first!" teased Jake. He pushed Tad out of the way, reached into the dark chamber, and groped around inside. "I've got something," he exclaimed.

When he pulled out a silver trophy, Tad ran for the door. "Stop him!" yelled Jake.

Chip jumped in front of Tad who bounced off of the android and started crying.

"Did I hurt you?" asked Chip. "I'm not supposed to hurt anyone."

Tad didn't answer. He covered his face and cried. Jake reached into the hole and pulled out more trophies. "What are those?" asked Chip.

"They're Mr. Duckworth's trophies," answered Jake. "It looks like Tad stole them and hid them here. Nice carpentry job, Taggart!"

"Shut up, shut up, shut up!" Tad wailed.
Beep-beep-beep.

"What *is* that blasted noise?" said Jake. "It's coming from inside here, but it's too dark to see. Chip, your shoulders are narrower than mine. Squeeze in there and find out what it is. I'll make sure Tad doesn't run away."

Chip stepped over to the secret hole in the wall and turned on his infrared vision. He could

137

easily see inside. "There's a computer in here," he reported.

"So it *was* you!" Jake exclaimed.

Suddenly the strange beeping stopped. The drop of root beer that had leaked inside Chip's body had finally evaporated. The internal interface radio stopped broadcasting and his circuits returned to normal. His voltages returned to their original levels and a quick internal scan showed Chip that all his systems were operating at standard levels. The strange beeping had come from the hidden computer which had picked up Chip's high-powered radio signals and rebroadcast them through its speaker.

Now that Chip's internal radio was no longer broadcasting automatically, it was able to receive a message from Dr. Carson. "Where are you, Chip? I've been trying to call you, but the radio's been beeping like a burglar alarm!"

"I'm at Tad Taggart's house," Chip answered.

Dr. Carson sighed heavily. "You've got to come home right now. The only way I can convince the police you're innocent is to show them that you're an android. Unless they find the real thief before you get home, I've failed."

"The thief is here," said the android.

"What? Who is it?" Dr. Carson cried.

"Tad Taggart," answered Chip. "The computer and the trophies were hidden in his room."

138

"Don't move, I'll be right there!" Dr. Carson said.

Chip stood perfectly still, his arms still inside the hole. "Hey, come out of there," said Jake. "We've got to figure out what to do with this little thief."

"I can't move," replied Chip, but his voice was muffled and Jake didn't hear him.

"Don't tell anybody I stole everything," pleaded Tad. "I'll give you half of everything I win from the video game contest if you don't tell. The grand prize is five thousand dollars. I only took the computer because I couldn't get enough time to work on it at school. The other kids wanted to use it too."

Jake laughed. "You'll never win that contest! Anything else hidden in there?" he said to Chip.

The android scanned the inner walls. "There are some cans of food in here."

"What?" said Jake. "I can't hear you. Are you going to stay in there all day?"

"There are some cans of food," yelled the android. "I can't get out."

"Are you stuck? What kind of food?"

"No," Chip replied. "Pineapple rings, canned cherries, and chocolate syrup."

"He must have taken those from the cafeteria," concluded Jake. "You're a weird kid, Taggart."

"I didn't mean to set the oven on fire. I was

139

working all night on the computer at school and I got hungry. I just wanted to fix myself something to eat. I had to bring those home with me because they had my fingerprints on them. Please don't tell anybody."

"I ought to put you in that hole and nail it up," growled Jake. "You planted that manual in Chip's book bag so everybody would think he was the thief. Then you had me buy those disks so I'd look suspicious, too."

Before Tad could answer, his mother opened the door. She looked very upset. "Tad," she said, "the police are downstairs. They want to see you. Do you have any idea why they're here?"

"Send them up," said Jake. "We've got a surprise for them."

"No!" yelled Tad. "Tell them I'm not here!"

Mrs. Taggart glanced around the room and spotted the hole in the wall. "Tad! What have you done to the wall! Do you know how much that will cost to fix?"

"Mrs. Taggart!" a voice called from downstairs. "Is your son up there?"

"Yes, he is," replied Mrs. Taggart. "You can come up."

Two police officers entered the room. Dr. Carson was behind them. "Chip, what are you doing?" he asked.

"I'm looking at the stolen computer," said the android. "Can I move now?"

"Bring it out," said his father.

Chip lifted the computer and carried it into the room. One of the cops turned it over and examined it. "The serial number matches," she said. "That's Harbor Junior High's computer all right!"

"Don't forget about these!" said Jake, holding up one of the trophies. "This is as close as he'll ever get to winning one."

"Mrs. Taggart," said the other officer, "I'm afraid your boy will have to come with us. It looks like he's responsible for the robberies at the school."

"I don't believe it," she cried. "Tad couldn't steal anything. There must be some other explanation."

"That's right," said Tad, thinking quickly. "Jake and Chip stole the computer and forced me to hide it here. They swore they'd beat me up if I didn't do what they asked."

"Can you prove it?" asked the officer.

"Can they prove they didn't steal the computer?" snapped Tad.

"Sure we can," said Jake confidently. "According to what the janitor said in the paper, the computer was stolen around four-thirty yesterday. Chip and I were at the Hamilton Street fruit market until after five o'clock."

"He's lying!" yelled Tad.

"We'll see about that," said the female officer. "The police officers investigating this case

141

last night weren't able to contact the market clerk today, but I can try again. Is there a phone we can use?"

"There's one in the hall," answered Tad's mother. "I'm sure my son is innocent."

"I'll get to the bottom of this," replied the cop. She picked up the phone.

Everyone was silent. "This is Officer Bailey of the Harbor City Police," she said. "Let me speak to whoever was working at your store yesterday between four and six p.m." After a long pause, she asked, "Do you remember seeing two boys in your store yesterday?" She looked over at Chip and Jake, examining them closely. "Both about thirteen years old. One blond with blue eyes, medium build. The other dark-haired, tall, broad-shouldered."

There was another long pause. Tad twisted his shirt in his hands, Dr. Carson chewed on the end of his glasses, Jake tapped his foot, Mrs. Taggart paced across the room, and Chip stood perfectly still and silent. Finally the officer spoke. "You're sure you don't remember? It's very important. All right, thank you—"

"Wait!" yelled Jake. "Ask him if he remembers the kid who knocked down all his oranges!"

"Oh, one more question," Officer Bailey quickly added. "How about a kid knocking down your oranges? He did? *Now* you remember! And the other one too? Do you remember when they left? Thank you very much, you've been a big help."

Coming back into the room, she said, "The man at the fruit market confirms that both of these boys were in his place when the crime was committed. I'm sorry, Mrs. Taggart."

"But Tad's such a good boy!" she wailed.

"You'd be surprised at some of the things I've seen good boys do," replied the officer.

Tad hung his head. "But I've never done anything wrong before! I only stole the trophies so I could sell them, buy my own computer, and win the video game contest. But then I found out I couldn't sell them anywhere. I tried to work on the computer at school at night, but it was too hard. I was going to give back the computer when I won the contest. Honest!"

But Officer Bailey read Tad his rights and added, "You'll have to come down to the station with us. Stealing is a serious offense."

Jake reached inside the secret panel and took out the large can of chocolate syrup. "He's also the one who set the cafeteria on fire!"

Officer Bailey shook her head in amazement. Then she led Tad downstairs, with Mrs. Taggart close behind. Dr. Carson, Chip, and Jake carried the computer and trophies. "Don't forget the chocolate syrup, Chip," said Dr. Carson. "It's evidence."

"Does that mean I'm a chocolate chip?" asked the android.

"Only if you spill it on yourself," said Jake, handing him the can. "Careful, the lid's loose."

Outside, as the officers were putting Tad in the police car, Chip's object-detection program saw Becky running down the sidewalk.

"Oh, Chip, you're innocent!" she cried, throwing her arms around his neck.

"Hey, careful," said Jake. "You'll spill the chocolate syrup."

"So what?" said Becky. "I'm just happy that my brother's all right."

"What about me?" Jake said. "I'm all right too!"

Chip's verbal response program analyzed what they both said, and he replied, "If I'm half right, and Jake's half right, then together we're all right."

They all laughed. Suddenly Becky said, "Oh, no. Look who's coming!"

The android turned around quickly. His pattern-recognition program told him that Mr. Duckworth was racing straight toward him!

"Finally I've caught up with you!" he yelled.

"Stop!" cried Becky.

Mr. Duckworth made a dive for Chip, but the android quickly dodged to the side. The gym teacher tumbled to the ground, crashing into the can of chocolate syrup, and it poured over him.

"I'll get you for this," sputtered Mr. Duckworth, wiping chocolate from his eyes.

"Here's one of your trophies. The police have the others," said Jake, handing him a silver cup. "Tad Taggart is the thief."

"What, what, what?" was all the startled man could say.

Chip examined the gym teacher sprawled across the lawn. "Is he a chocolate duck?" he asked.

"That's not a nice way to talk about teachers," said Dr. Carson, hardly able to keep from laughing. "Come on, son, let's go home."

The police took the empty can of syrup, but Mr. Duckworth wouldn't let them have the trophy. "I'm not letting it out of my sight!" he shouted, clutching it tightly against his chocolate-covered chest as he struggled to his feet.

Jake slapped Chip on the back as the police drove away with Tad and Mrs. Taggart. "Well, I've got to get going or Mom and Dad will rent out my room."

"Goodbye," said Chip. He paused as his electrologic index of conflict resolution finally solved a problem that he had been working on for the past several minutes. "You're my friend," he added, "not Tad."

"Thanks," Jake replied. "You're my friend too."

"I hope this means you two won't be fighting anymore," said Dr. Carson.

"Don't worry," sighed Jake. "Every time I try to sock him, he just dodges out of the way. Chip should be on the school boxing team."

"Do they make boxes?" asked the android.

"Oooh," groaned Jake. "Your puns are really killers."

"I'm not supposed to hurt people," said Chip.

"I think I'll live. See you later." Jake turned and ran down the block. "Goodbye," he called over his shoulder.

"Maybe you should let him hit you once in a while," Dr. Carson said to Chip. "You don't want to be too perfect, or people will suspect you're not quite human."

"Oh, Pops!" said Becky. "If Jake ever hit Chip, he'd break his hand!"

"I guess I build them to last," said the scientist proudly. "Come on, kids, let's go home and order a pizza."

"What will you order it to do?" asked Chip.

"I'm going to tell it to jump in my mouth," replied his father.

"Me too," said Becky laughing. "I'm so hungry I could eat an elephant."

"It wouldn't fit in your mouth," Chip said, as they began walking home.

146

"Okay," replied Becky. "A baby elephant!"

Later that fall . . .

Desperately trying to balance himself, Chip tripped over backward and hit the floor. *Wham!*

"Nails!" shouted Brian. "I didn't see you come in. Did you do that?"

"What do you think?" Nails stood over Chip. He was wearing a black leather jacket and had had his hair cut in a Mohawk. A big gold earring dangled from one ear. "Nobody else plays these drums but me. Nobody even *touches* them!"

"Chip! Are you okay?" yelled Becky frantically.

Can Chip stand up to a bully like Nails? Will Erin find out that he's NOT QUITE HUMAN? Find out in Book #2: *All Geared Up,* available now.